IDENTIFICATION METHODS FOR MICROBIOLOGISTS

PART A

THE SOCIETY FOR APPLIED BACTERIOLOGY
TECHNICAL SERIES NO. 1

IDENTIFICATION METHODS FOR MICROBIOLOGISTS

Edited by

B. M. GIBBS

*Unilever Research Laboratory, Colworth House
Sharnbrook, Bedfordshire, England*

AND

F. A. SKINNER

*Rothamsted Experimental Station, Harpenden
Hertfordshire, England*

PART A

1966

ACADEMIC PRESS · LONDON · NEW YORK

ACADEMIC PRESS INC. (LONDON) LTD
BERKELEY SQUARE HOUSE
BERKELEY SQUARE
LONDON, W.1

U.S. Edition published by
ACADEMIC PRESS INC.
111 FIFTH AVENUE
NEW YORK, NEW YORK 10003

Library of Congress Catalog Card Number: 66–20871

Printed in Great Britain by
W. & J. Mackay & Co. Ltd., Chatham, Kent

Contributors

A. C. BAIRD-PARKER, *Unilever Research Laboratory, Colworth House, Sharnbrook, Bedford, England*

ELLA M. BARNES, *Low Temperature Research Station, Cambridge, England*

IRENE BATTY, *The Wellcome Research Laboratories, Beckenham, Kent, England*

D. C. CANN, *Ministry of Technology, Torry Research Station, Aberdeen, Scotland*

K. PATRICIA CARPENTER, *Central Public Health Laboratory, Colindale, London, England*

PATRICIA H. CLARKE, *Biochemistry Department, University College, London, England*

T. CROSS, *Department of Biological Sciences, Bradford Instiutte of Technology, Bradford, Yorkshire, England*

T. F. FRYER, *National Institute for Research in Dairying, Shinfield, Reading, Berkshire, England*

H. S. GOLDBERG, *Department of Microbiology, School of Medicine, University of Missouri, U.S.A.*

M. GOODFELLOW, *Hartley Botanical Laboratories, The University, Liverpool, England*

S. G. M. GOWER, *Ministry of Agriculture, Fisheries and Food, Central Veterinary Laboratory, Weybridge, Surrey, England*

T. R. G. GRAY, *Hartley Botanical Laboratories, The University, Liverpool, England*

A. C. HAYWARD, *Commonwealth Mycological Institute, Kew, Surrey, England*

MARGARET S. HENDRIE, *Ministry of Technology, Torry Research Station, Aberdeen, Scotland*

G. HOBBS, *Ministry of Technology, Torry Research Station, Aberdeen, Scotland*

C. S. IMPEY, *Low Temperature Research Station, Cambridge, England*

L. JEFFRIES, *Vitamins Limited, Walton Oaks Experimental Station, Tadworth, Surrey, England*

S. P. LAPAGE, *Central Public Health Laboratory, Colindale, London, England*

A. M. MACIVER, *Department of Biological Sciences, Bradford Institute of Technology, Bradford, Yorkshire, England*

W. J. Brinley Morgan, *Ministry of Agriculture, Fisheries and Food, Central Veterinary Laboratory, Weybridge, Surrey, England*

R. J. Olds, *Department of Pathology, Cambridge, England*

S. A. Price, *Vitamins Limited, Walton Oaks Experimental Station, Tadworth, Surrey, England*

M. Elisabeth Sharpe, *National Institute for Research in Dairying, Shinfield, Reading, Berkshire, England*

J. M. Shewan, *Ministry of Technology, Torry Research Station, Aberdeen, Scotland*

D. G. Smith, *Queen Elizabeth College, London, England*

P. H. A. Sneath, *MRC Microbial Systematics Research Unit, Leicester University, University Road, Leicester, England*

K. J. Steel, *Central Public Health Laboratory, Colindale, London, England*

P. D. Walker, *The Wellcome Research Laboratories, Beckenham, Kent, England*

P. Ridgway Watt, *Vitamins Limited, Walton Oaks Experimental Station, Tadworth, Surrey, England*

Preface

On the 27th October 1964 the Society for Applied Bacteriology in accordance with now established custom, held an autumn demonstration meeting, though on this occasion the meeting was organized jointly with the Microbial Systematics Group of the Society for General Microbiology. Following this meeting the organizers were made aware of a feeling among members that a useful purpose would be served by bringing together accounts of the various techniques demonstrated and publishing them. This Manual is the result of the joint decision of both Societies to publish.

The editors would like to record their particular thanks to Dr A. C. Hayward, Secretary of the Microbial Systematics Group, for his help in organizing the meeting, and to Dr A. H. Dadd and his staff at Imperial College for their considerable help with the laboratory arrangements. Grateful thanks are also due to the contributors for their willingness to submit exhibits in the first place, and later for providing typescripts that had not originally been solicited. Despite the imperfections and shortcomings of this volume the editors hope that it will assist, especially at the bench, those whose task it is to distinguish one bacterial species from another.

January 1966

B. M. GIBBS
F. A. SKINNER

Contents

Foreword

WHILE there are many excellent textbooks covering bacteriological methods, and most published papers give details of the methods used, there is often a "missing link"—that is, the opportunity personally to meet the inventor or user of a new or modified method, to see what apparatus and reagents he uses, to observe the resulting specimens and results, and to discuss with him the advantages and disadvantages relative to the work in hand. To forge this missing link the Society for Applied Bacteriology decided some years ago to hold a meeting devoted to the demonstration and discussion of techniques used in the bacteriological laboratory. Techniques in current use were shown by those experienced in their use and difficulties likely to be met, either in performance or in the interpretation of results, were discussed. Similar meetings have been held each year and so useful have these "demonstration" meetings proved that they have become an annual event on the bacteriological calendar.

Of the methods and results so far exhibited and discussed some have been new, some old, some modified and some resurrected. The common link is that all contributors have been experts in their particular fields of microbiology. They have described techniques which they themselves use in their everyday work because, at the present time, they have found them to give reasonably reliable results.

As time progressed it became clear that the Society needed a permanent record of these techniques in a form readily available to those wishing to make use of them. It was therefore decided to break new ground with the publication of the present manual.

The methods described within these covers represent but a fraction of those needed in the laboratory. It is the Society's intention to publish in further manuals additional methods which specialists have found to be most useful.

All laboratory methods are subject to change or modification in the light of new knowledge, or with the introduction of new tests. In course of time therefore this and succeeding manuals will inevitably need to be revised.

It is hoped that these manuals will provide up-to-date reliable information for those at the bench. Micro-organisms, like people, usually behave in a proper manner when examined in a reasonable way.

JOAN TAYLOR
President, Society for Applied Bacteriology

The Identification of Certain *Pseudomonas* Species

Margaret S. Hendrie and J. M. Shewan

Ministry of Technology, Torry Research Station, Aberdeen, Scotland

In the past, the identification of pseudomonads has presented many problems. Detailed studies have been made of the taxonomy of a few species, e.g. *Pseudomonas aeruginosa* (Haynes, 1951; Liston *et al.*, 1963) and *Pseudomonas fluorescens* (Rhodes, 1959), and more general studies have also been made (Lysenko, 1961; Colwell and Liston, 1961). With a view to clarifying the overall classification of the group, a dichotomous key has been produced to split it into its major divisions. In order to give a specific name to a particular organism, it will be necessary to use one of the standard reference books (e.g. Bergey's Manual) or to refer to the literature.

In formulating this key (Fig. 1) the following methods have been used:

(1) Microscopic examination of cultures grown in liquid and solid media to determine motility, morphology and Gram reaction.

(2) Electron-microscopic examination for the arrangement of flagella.

(3) Colonial morphology and pigmentation on nutrient agar.

(4) Examination of nutrient agar and broth cultures by ultra-violet light for fluorescence.

(5) Oxidase test of Kovacs (1956).

(6) Attack on glucose, tested by the method of Hugh and Leifson (1953).

(7) Identity of the type of diffusible pigment by use of the media of King *et al.* (1954).

(8) Enhancement of diffusible pigment production by the method of Paton (1959).

(9) Ability to grow at 42°C by the method suggested by Haynes and Rhodes (1962).

(10) Ability to fix atmospheric nitrogen by growth on the nitrogen-free medium of Norris (1959).

(11) Enhancement of non-diffusible pigments by growth on special media (usually the inclusion of glucose or other carbohydrate in a peptone medium).

(12) Ability to break down oxalate by clearing the medium of Bhat and Barker (1948).

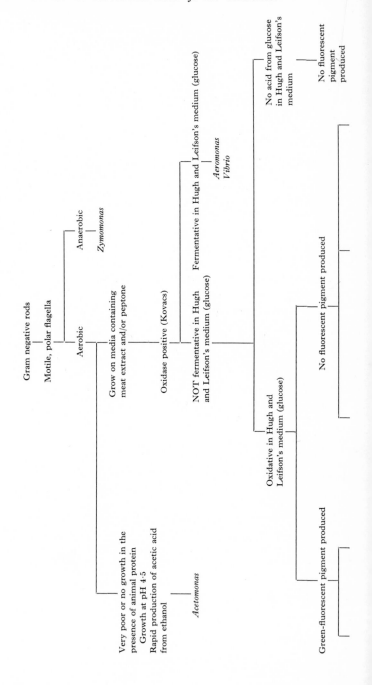

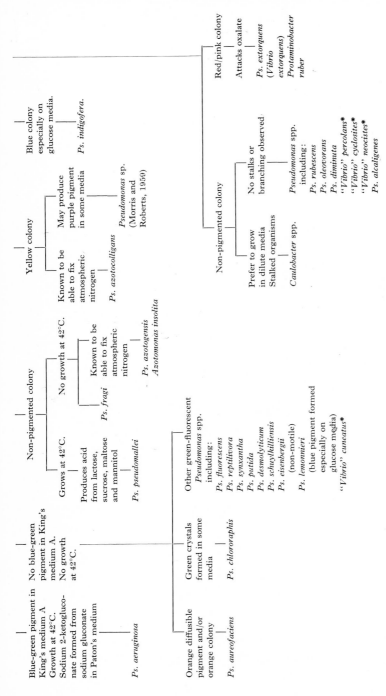

FIG. 1.

* These species are no longer considered to be *Vibrio* spp.

Certain groups of organisms have been deliberately excluded from this key. These are:

(a) Plant pathogenic *Pseudomonas* and *Xanthomonas* species, which although conforming to the majority of the features, have not been studied by us.

(b) Groups which require special growth conditions, e.g. *Halobacterium*, *Methanomonas*, etc.

Other groups, although not excluded from the key, are not discussed in detail. These include *Acetomonas* and the *Aeromonas—Vibrio* group. The differentiation of these genera from *Pseudomonas* has been described previously by Shimwell *et al.* (1960) for *Acetomonas* and Shewan *et al.* (1960) for the *Aeromonas—Vibrio* group.

In identifying *Pseudomonas* spp. the following features are considered important:

(i) Gram-negative rods, motile by means of polar flagella.

(ii) Colonies generally achromogenic and may or may not produce diffusible fluorescent pigment, but chromogenic species may occur in both the fluorescent and non-fluorescent groups.

(iii) Positive reaction in the oxidase test (Kovacs, 1956).

(iv) Reaction on carbohydrate on the medium of Hugh and Leifson (1953).

(v) Identity of diffusible pigments.

(vi) Ability to grow at certain temperatures.

Although most of the known pseudomonads can be classified using this series of tests, there are a few exceptions, e.g. plant pathogens and *Pseudomonas maltophilia*. Several of the plant pathogenic *Pseudomonas* spp. are oxidase-negative. This may be due to the absence of cytochrome c in the cell (D'Aubert, 1963). *Pseudomonas maltophilia* (Hugh and Ryschenkow, 1961) is also oxidase-negative. However, recent data appear to indicate that this species should not be included in the pseudomonas group (De Ley, 1964).

Yellow- and orange-pigmented organisms have also been encountered, and some of these types have been included in the key, e.g. *Pseudomonas* spp. (Morris and Roberts, 1959) and *Pseudomonas aureofaciens* (Kluyver, 1956). These are believed to be *Pseudomonas* spp. rather than *Xanthomonas* spp., as they are not plant pathogens. The pigments of some of these organisms have not been examined, but it is now believed that the carotenoid pigments of *Xanthomonas* are genus-specific (Starr and Stephens, 1964). The position of the yellow-pigmented *Pseudomonas saccharophila* in the pseudomonas group is uncertain. Recent data on the deoxyribonucleic acid base composition appear to suggest that it does not come within the group (Marmur *et al.*, 1963).

The ability to fix atmospheric nitrogen is listed as diagnostic of certain species. It is possible that some pseudomonads other than those named in the key may have this property (Proctor and Wilson, 1958; L'vov, 1963).

It should be emphasized that with a dichotomous key there are bound to be exceptions to the diagnostic features. Thus *Pseudomonas eisenbergii* is non-motile, but is green-fluorescent and in other features is very similar to *Pseudomonas fluorescens* (cf. Rhodes, 1959). *Pseudomonas aeruginosa* can exhibit any one of a number of variations, e.g. it can (1) be non-motile; (2) be fluorescent, but produce no pyocyanin; (3) produce no diffusible pigments; (4) produce pyorubin in place of pyocyanin; (5) be non-motile and fluorescent, but produce no pyocyanin; and (6) be non-motile, fluorescent and produce a melanin-like pigment (Liu, 1962). In some cases the final diagnosis of this species appears to depend on its ability to grow at 42°C and it is therefore easy to confuse it with other species such as *Ps. fluorescens* (Rhodes, 1959) and *Ps. chlororaphis* (Haynes and Rhodes, 1962).

It is well known that a dichotomous key is based on the idea that micro-organisms can be placed in monothetic groups which "are formed by rigid and successive logical divisions so that the possession of a unique set of features is both sufficient and necessary for membership in the group thus defined" (Sokal and Sneath, 1963). The new ideas introduced by numerical taxonomy would overcome these difficulties by a polythetic arrangement in which organisms that have the greatest number of shared features are placed together, and no single feature is essential for group membership or sufficient to make an organism a member of the group (Sokal and Sneath, 1963). When more information has been accumulated it should be possible to state the probability of an organism possessing any feature given in the diochotomous key and so producing a more natural grouping of the organisms.

The generic name *Comamonas* as proposed by Davis and Park (1962) has not been used in the preparation of the key. It would, in fact, cover the strains listed as *Pseudomonas* spp. which produce no acid from glucose in Hugh and Leifson's medium. The position of the red or pink pigmented oxalate decomposers in the genus may be doubtful as these species do not attack glucose oxidatively, but they do attack glycerol in this manner in Hugh and Leifson's medium (cf. Hayward, 1960).

Several species have been listed as "*Vibrio*". It has been recognized for a number of years that these species do not fit the genus *Vibrio* (Hugh and Leifson, 1953; Shewan *et al.*, 1960; Davis and Park, 1962). In fact, the original names given by Gray and Thornton (1928) to their isolates were recognized by the authors as temporary. These authors state:

"It is no part of the present work to give the bacteria isolated a permanent classification; indeed it seems that with our present knowledge and methods a satisfactory classification of bacteria cannot be arrived at. The system here adopted is therefore one of convenience only and its temporary nature is recognised."

Electron microscope examination of representative strains was carried out by Mr W. Hodgkiss.

The work described in this paper was carried out as part of the programme of the Department of Scientific and Industrial Research.

References

BHAT, J. V., & BARKER, H. A. (1948). Studies on a new oxalate-decomposing bacterium, *Vibrio oxaliticus*. *J. Bact.*, **55**, 359.

COLWELL, R. R., & LISTON, J. (1961). Taxonomic relationships among the pseudomonads. *J. Bact.*, **82**, 1.

D'AUBERT, S. (1963). Ricerche sulle ossidasi degli schizomiceti. *Ann. Microbiol. Milano.*, **13**, 85.

DAVIS, G. H. G., & PARK, R. W. A. (1962). A taxonomic study of certain bacteria currently classified as *Vibrio* species. *J. gen. Microbiol.*, **27**, 101.

DE LEY, J. (1964). *Pseudomonas* and related genera. *Annu. Rev. Microbiol.*, **18**, 17.

GRAY, P. H. H., & THORNTON, H. G. (1928). Soil bacteria that decompose certain aromatic compounds. *Zbl. Bakt. Abt. II*, **73**, 74.

HAYNES, W. C. (1951). *Pseudomonas aeruginosa*—its characterization and identification. *J. gen. Microbiol.*, **5**, 939.

HAYNES, W. C., & RHODES, L. J. (1962). Comparative taxonomy of crystallogenic strains of *Pseudomonas aeruginosa* and *Pseudomonas chlororaphis*. *J. Bact.*, **84**, 1080.

HAYWARD, A. C. (1960). Relationship between *Protaminobacter ruber* and some red-pigmented pseudomonads. *J. appl. Bact.*, **23**, xii.

HUGH, R., & LEIFSON, E. (1953). The taxonomic significance of fermentative versus oxidative metabolism of carbohydrates by various Gram-negative bacteria. *J. Bact.*, **66**, 24.

HUGH, R., & RYSCHENKOW, E. (1961). *Pseudomonas maltophilia*, an Alcaligenes-like species. *J. gen. Microbiol.*, **26**, 123.

KING, E. O., WARD, M. K., & RANEY, D. E. (1954). Two simple media for the demonstration of pyocyanin and fluorescin. *J. Lab. Clin. Med.*, **44**, 301.

KLUYVER, A. J. (1956). *Pseudomonas aureofaciens* nov. spec. and its pigments. *J. Bact.*, **72**, 406.

KOVACS, N. (1956). Identification of *Pseudomonas pyocyanea* by the oxidase reaction. *Nature, Lond.*, **178**, 703.

LISTON, J., WIEBE, W., & COLWELL, R. R. (1963). Quantitative approach to the study of bacterial species. *J. Bact.*, **85**, 1061.

LIU, P. V. (1962). Non-motile varieties of *Pseudomonas aeruginosa* producing melanin-like pigment. *J. Bact.*, **84**, 378.

L'VOV, N. P. (1963). New free-living nitrogen-fixing micro-organisms. *Izv. Akad. Nauk SSSR, Ser. biol.*, **2**, 270.

LYSENKO, O. (1961). *Pseudomonas*—An attempt at a general classification. *J. gen. Microbiol.*, **25**, 379.

MARMUR, J., FALKOW, S., & MANDEL, M. (1963). New approaches to bacterial taxonomy. *Annu. Rev. Microbiol.*, **17**, 329.

MORRIS, M. B., & ROBERTS, J. B. (1959). A group of pseudomonads able to synthesise poly-β-hydroxybutyric acid. *Nature, Lond.*, **183**, 1538.

NORRIS, J. R. (1959). The isolation and identification of Azotobacters. *Lab. Pract.*, **8**, 239.

PATON, A. M. (1959). Enhancement of pigment production by *Pseudomonas*. *Nature, Lond.*, **184**, 1254.

PROCTOR, M. H., & WILSON, P. W. (1958). Nitrogen fixation by Gram negative bacteria. *Nature, Lond.*, **182**, 891.

RHODES, M. E. (1959). The characterization of *Pseudomonas fluorescens*. *J. gen. Microbiol.*, **21**, 221.

SHEWAN, J. M., HOBBS, G., & HODGKISS, W. (1960). A determinative scheme for the identification of certain genera of Gram-negative bacteria, with special reference to the Pseudomonadaceae. *J. appl. Bact.*, **23**, 379.

SHIMWELL, J. L., CARR, J. G., & RHODES, M. E. (1960). Differentiation of *Acetomonas* and *Pseudomonas*. *J. gen. Microbiol.*, **23**, 283.

SOKAL, R. R., & SNEATH, P. H. A. (1963). *Principles of numerical taxonomy*, p. 13. London: W. H. Freeman & Co.

STARR, M. P., & STEPHENS, W. L. (1964). Pigmentation and taxonomy of the genus *Xanthomonas*. *J. Bact.*, **87**, 293.

Methods of Identification in the Genus *Xanthomonas*

A. C. HAYWARD*

Commonwealth Mycological Institute, Kew, Surrey, England

The genus *Xanthomonas* is a genus of plant pathogens. Some species are apparently world-wide in distribution, e.g. *X. campestris* (black rot of crucifers), but others are more restricted. In the seventh edition of *Bergey's Manual of Determinative Bacteriology* (Breed *et al.*, 1957) about sixty species are listed. Since this edition more than forty additional species have been described in the literature. There are apparently records of only four species in the British Isles: *X. campestris*, *X. begoniae*, *X. juglandis*, and *X. hyacinthi*.

Xanthomonas speciation has been based on proved or assumed host specificity. This concept is now widely held to be unreliable because:

(1) Xanthomonads are physiologically relatively homogeneous and there is, in general, no consistent physiological basis for species differentiation. It is usually impossible to identify a species when it is separated from the host of origin. Species from diverse hosts may be indistinguishable in the laboratory. Where there is physiological variation in a collection of isolates from one host (i.e. one "species") the variation is frequently as great as that between any other species. This conclusion follows from the work of Dye (1962, 1963a).

(2) Although the evidence on this point is conflicting, it appears that virulence and pathogenicity may not be stable characters (Wernham, 1948; Dye, 1958; Logan, 1960). The work of Dye (1958) suggests that species of *Xanthomonas* may be adapted to hosts other than the host of origin by plant passage.

(3) Species of *Xanthomonas* have been shown by numerical taxonomy to form a group distinct at the generic level from *Pseudomonas*, but too closely clustered to justify the numerous species in the literature (Colwell and Liston, 1961).

Identification at the Generic Level

Most workers are agreed that xanthomonads have the following characters in common:

* *Present address:* Department of Microbiology, Medical School, Herston, Brisbane, Qld, Australia.

(1) Aerobic, Gram-negative rods, motile by a single polar flagellum.

(2) They produce a yellow, water-insoluble pigment on agar medium.

According to Starr and Stephens (1964) the pigment is a unique caro-tenoid alcohol which is not found in any yellow non-xanthomonad. They showed that the extracted carotenoid has absorption maxima at 418, 437, and 463 mμ in petroleum ether. There are rare exceptions which do not produce any pigment; for example, some strains of *X. ricini*, and *X. manihotis*.

(3) They have an oxidative metabolism of carbohydrates (Hugh and Leifson, 1953). The medium recommended for the determination of carbo-hydrate utilization by *Xanthomonas* spp. is that used by Dye (1962), or alternatively that used by Hayward (1964a, 1964b); the medium used by Hugh and Leifson usually gives a less clear cut result. Yellow-pigmented bacteria with a growth rate more rapid than that of xanthomonads are common on moribund plant material: these bacteria have not infrequently been confused with *Xanthomonas*, but they possess an anaerogenic, fermentative metabolism of carbohydrates, and when motile have peri-trichous flagella. Dye has recently transferred to the genus *Erwinia* two species, *E. uredovora* and *E. stewartii*, which are both fermentative, but which were previously, and inappropriately, classified in the genus *Xantho-monas* (Pon *et al.*, 1954; Hayward and Hodgkiss, 1961; Dye, 1963b, 1963c).

In addition, the following characters are found in the majority of species in the genus *Xanthomonas*:

(1) Failure to produce nitrite from nitrate. There are reports in the literature of xanthomonads which produce nitrite from nitrate, but the rigorous tests carried out by Dye (1962) have failed to confirm these observations in a single case.

(2) Failure to decompose nitrite.

(3) Failure to produce indole or acetoin.

(4) Failure to produce urease.

(5) Failure to hydrolyse sodium hippurate.

(6) Failure to produce a UV-fluorescent, diffusible pigment.

(7) Catalase is produced.

(8) Aesculin is hydrolysed (on prolonged incubation of up to 30 days in some cases).

(9) Oxidase-negative or weakly positive by the method of Kovacs (1956).

(10) Lipolytic activity. Most species are strongly lipolytic.

Species of *Xanthomonas* are variable in the following characteristics:

(1) Proteolytic activity. Most species are proteolytic, although to a vary-ing extent. Non-proteolytic species are known.

(2) Starch hydrolysis. As in *Bacillus* (Smith *et al.*, 1952), there is marked variation; species which give a strong and clearly defined zone of hydrolysis on starch agar predominate, a minority of species give a restricted reaction on starch agar, and still fewer give no reaction at all.

(3) Utilization of specific carbohydrates. Lactose-positive and lactose-negative strains of *Xanthomonas malvacearum* are known, for example (Hayward, 1964a). The majority of species of *Xanthomonas* oxidize glucose, sucrose, fructose, galactose, mannose, arabinose, and cellobiose. There is variation between species, and sometimes between different isolates of the same species, in oxidation of xylose, lactose, melibiose, dextrin, maltose, raffinose, and mannitol (Dye, 1962).

(4) Production of enzymes hydrolysing pectin and pectic acid. A minority of *Xanthomonas* spp. produce pectin methyl esterase and polygalacturonase (Smith, 1958; Dye, 1960).

(5) Nutritional requirements. *X. pruni* has a requirement for nicotinic acid in a defined medium and *X. albilineans* a requirement for methionine and glutamic acid (Starr, 1946).

(6) Lysis by bacteriophages. *Xanthomonas* bacteriophages vary in specificity perhaps depending on the source of the phage. Phages from infected plant material alone often appear to be highly specific, whereas those isolated from soil or sewage may lyse many species of *Xanthomonas* (Sutton *et al.*, 1958; Hayward, 1964a).

(7) Production of a brown, diffusible, melanin-like pigment in a medium containing tyrosine. Examples include *X. phaseoli* var. *fuscans*, *X. ricini* (some strains), *X. punicae*, *X. geranii*, and *X. pelargonii* (Dye, 1962).

(8) Colony form. In general xanthomonads give a characteristic shiny, mucoid growth on agar medium containing a utilizable carbohydrate, but some strains are more mucoid than others. The colour and consistency of the colonies also varies between strains; these features are sometimes useful in identification.

Identification at the Specific Level

This is based on a comparison of the cultural and physiological characteristics of fresh isolates from plant material with those of authentic cultures from the same host, and upon the reaction of the host of origin to the isolate on artificial inoculation. This is clearly unsatisfactory, but is the logical consequence of the present concept of species in *Xanthomonas*. Although definition of species is apparently not possible using physiological tests, some tests are nevertheless useful in identification, that is to say there are consistent differences between isolates of one species and sometimes between isolates of different species.

Techniques for the routine examination of xanthomonads

Starch hydrolysis

The recommended medium is: Peptone (Oxoid, Oxo Ltd., London), 5·0 g; yeast extract (Difco), 3·0 g; soluble starch (British Drug Houses Ltd.) 2·0 g; agar (Oxoid No. 3), 15·0 g; distilled water, 1 litre. The pH is adjusted to ca. 7·2, and the medium dispensed in 1-oz bottles, 20 ml per bottle. The agar is poured into 9-cm diam Petri dishes and 3 cavities per plate are punched out of the agar with a No. 2 cork borer. The cavities are inoculated at the centre with a 3-mm diam wire loop loaded with inoculum from a heavy suspension in sterile distilled water. After 3–6 days at 28°C the plates are flooded with an iodine/potassium iodide solution (e.g. Gram's iodine solution). With standardization of the inoculum size the method can be used to obtain a crude quantitative measure of activity of different isolates by measuring the diameter of the zones of hydrolysis. Some xanthomonads, for example *X. holcicola*, *X. pruni*, and some strains of *X. vasculorum*, do not give a clearly defined zone of hydrolysis, but give a diffuse zone of partial hydrolysis extending from the boundary of the confluent growth which is visible when the plate is held to the light (Hayward, 1962).

Casein and gelatin hydrolysis

The medium is: Peptone (Oxoid), 5·0 g; yeast extract (Difco), 3·0 g; agar (Oxoid), 15·0 g; distilled water, 1 litre. The pH is adjusted to ca 7·2 and the molten medium dispensed in 45-ml quantities in 2-oz bottles. Either 5 ml of 4% casein suspension (Judex, light white soluble) or 5 ml of 4% gelatin solution (British Drug Houses Ltd.) is added to the cooled basal medium and 3 plates are poured from each bottle. Plates are inoculated either by streaking or by inoculating cavities as described for the starch agar medium. After 3–6 days at 28° the gelatin plates are flooded with Frazier's acid mercuric chloride solution (Frazier, 1926). Zones of clearing on casein agar can be seen without the acid mercuric chloride treatment, but use of this reagent increases the clarity of the zones. This method is useful for the comparison of proteolytic activity of *Xanthomonas* spp; in *X. malvacearum*, for example, there are weakly proteolytic and strongly proteolytic strains which can be differentiated by this method (Hayward, 1964a).

Hydrolysis of Tween 80

The method described by Sierra (1957) is recommended. Tween 80, the polyoxyethylene derivative of sorbitan monooleate (Honeywill & Stein Ltd.), is made up as a 10% (w/v) solution and 5-ml quantities dispensed in

$\frac{1}{2}$-oz bottles. Five ml is added to 45 ml of molten, cooled basal medium and 3 plates are poured. Most *Xanthomonas* species give a clear, positive reaction in 2–6 days' incubation at 28°.

Maceration of potato slices

Large, firm, potato tubers are washed free of soil, dipped into 95% industrial spirit and flamed off. The tubers are peeled with a sterile scalpel and transverse sections about 7–8 mm thick are cut and placed in Petri dishes. A V-shaped groove is cut down the centre of the slice with a sterile scalpel and sterile distilled water is poured over the whole slice to a depth about half-way up the slice. A massive inoculum from growth on agar is streaked down the centre of the groove using a wire loop. Plates are incubated for 24–48 h at 25°. Macerating activity is tested by pricking the sides of the groove with a sterile loop. Some *Xanthomonas* spp. have strong macerating activity; for example, *X. campestris*, which also produces a blackening of the rotted tissue. Many other xanthomonads have no macerating activity. This is a crude method for the detection of pectolytic enzymes; other more refined methods are described by Smith (1958) and Dye (1960).

Other methods

The slimy, yellow, mucoid growth of *Xanthomonas* spp. is best seen on an agar medium containing either glucose or sucrose (20·0 g/l).

Media and methods for the production of brown diffusible pigment on a medium containing tyrosine, utilization of carbohydrates, aesculin hydrolysis, and lysis by bacteriophages, are given by Dye (1962, 1963a) and Hayward (1964a, 1964b).

References

BREED, R. S., MURRAY, E. G. D., & SMITH, N. R. (1957). *Bergey's Manual of Determinative Bacteriology*. 7th ed. London: Baillière, Tindall & Cox.

COLWELL, R. R., & LISTON, J. (1961). Taxonomic analysis with the electronic computer of some *Xanthomonas* and *Pseudomonas* species. *J. Bact.*, **82**, 913.

DYE, D. W. (1958). Host specificity in *Xanthomonas*. *Nature, Lond.*, **182**, 1813.

DYE, D. W. (1960). Pectolytic activity in *Xanthomonas*. *N.Z.Jl. Sci.*, **3**, 61.

DYE, D. W. (1962). The inadequacy of the usual determinative tests for the identification of *Xanthomonas* spp. *N.Z.Jl. Sci.*, **5**, 393.

DYE, D. W. (1963a). Comparative study of the biochemical reactions of additional *Xanthomonas* spp. *N.Z.Jl. Sci.*, **6**, 483.

DYE, D. W. (1963b). The taxonomic position of *Xanthomonas uredovorus* Pon et al. 1954. *N.Z.Jl. Sci.*, **6**, 146.

DYE, D. W. (1963c). The taxonomic position of *Xanthomonas stewartii* (Erw. Smith 1914) Dowson 1939. *N.Z.Jl. Sci.*, **6**, 495.

FRAZIER, W. C. (1926). A method for the detection of changes in gelatin due to bacteria. *J. infect. Dis.*, **39**, 302.

HAYWARD, A. C. (1962). Studies on bacterial pathogens of sugar cane. *Occ. Pap. Sug. Ind. Res. Inst., Mauritius*, **13**, 1.

HAYWARD, A. C. (1964a). Bacteriophage sensitivity and biochemical group in *Xanthomonas malvacearum*. *J. gen. Microbiol.*, **35**, 287.

HAYWARD, A. C. (1964b). Characteristics of *Pseudomonas solanacearum*. *J. appl. Bact.*, **27**, 265.

HAYWARD, A. C., & HODGKISS, W. (1961). Taxonomic relationships of *Xanthomonas uredovorus*. *J. gen. Microbiol.*, **26**, 133.

HUGH, R., & LEIFSON, E. (1953). The taxonomic significance of fermentative versus oxidative metabolism of carbohydrates by various Gram-negative bacteria. *J. Bact.*, **66**, 24.

KOVACS, N. (1956). Identification of *Pseudomonas pyocyanea* by the oxidase reaction. *Nature, Lond.*, **178**, 703.

LOGAN, C. (1960). Host specificity of two *Xanthomonas* species. *Nature, Lond.*, **188**, 479.

PON, D. S., TOWNSEND, C. E., WESSMAN, G. E., SCHMITT, C. G., & KINGSOLVER, C. H. (1954). A *Xanthomonas* parasitic on uredia of cereal rusts. *Phytopathology*, **44**, 707.

SIERRA, G. (1957). A simple method for the detection of lipolytic activity of micro-organisms and some observations on the influence of the contact between cells and fatty substrates. *Antonie van Leeuwenhock*, **23**, 15.

SMITH, W. K. (1958). A survey of the production of pectic enzymes by plant pathogenic and other bacteria. *J. gen. Microbiol.*, **18**, 33.

SMITH, W. R., GORDON, R. E., & CLARK, F. E. (1952). Aerobic Spore-forming Bacteria. *Agric. Monograph, U.S. Dep. Agric.*, 16.

STARR, M. P. (1946). The nutrition of phytopathogenic bacteria. I. Minimal nutritive requirements of the genus *Xanthomonas*. *J. Bact.*, **51**, 131.

STARR, M. P., & STEPHENS, W. L. (1964). Pigmentation and taxonomy of the genus *Xanthomonas*. *J. Bact.*, **87**, 293.

SUTTON, M. D., KATZNELSON, H., & QUADLING, C. (1958). A bacteriophage that attacks numerous Xanthomonas species. *Canad. J. Microbiol.*, **4**, 493.

WERNHAM, C. C. (1948). The species value of pathogenicity in the genus *Xanthomonas*. *Phytopathology*, **38**, 283.

Identification Methods applied to *Chromobacterium*

P. H. A. SNEATH

MRC Microbial Systematics Research Unit
Leicester University, University Road, Leicester, England

The genus *Chromobacterium* contains two well-defined species, *C. violaceum* and *C. lividum*. They are motile Gram-negative rods. For a general study see Sneath (1960); many details are also in Sneath (1956*a*, *b*) and Leifson (1956).

The genus is probably not a natural one. Some unpigmented bacteria resembling aeromonads or vibrios, and possibly some resembling agrobacteria or pseudomonads, may prove on closer study to be related to the two species mentioned above. Nevertheless, the two species do share some unusual features:

(1) Both produce the same violet pigment, violacein.
(2) Both have an unusual flagellar morphology.
(3) Both are highly sensitive to peroxides.

In practice strains are recognized initially by their pigment; if this is too faint to be noticed, the strains may be thought to belong to one of the other groups mentioned above.

Methods Useful in Recognizing Members of the Genus

The pigment violacein

Violacein is a complex indole-pyrrole pigment, found within the bacterial cells. Not all media give abundant pigment; glycerol, peptone, and suboptimal growth temperatures favour its production.

Violacein is insoluble in water and in chloroform, but is soluble in ethyl alcohol, giving a violet solution. To obtain this, shake pigmented culture with 96% ethyl alcohol and filter off the cells through filter paper. The solution shows an absorption maximum at 580 mμ and a minimum at 430 mμ. On adding 10% (v/v) of sulphuric acid (care!) the solution becomes green (absorption maximum at 700 mμ, see Fig. 1). If caustic soda is added it also becomes green, but rapidly turns red-brown and decomposes.

Spot-testing cultures for violacein is simple:

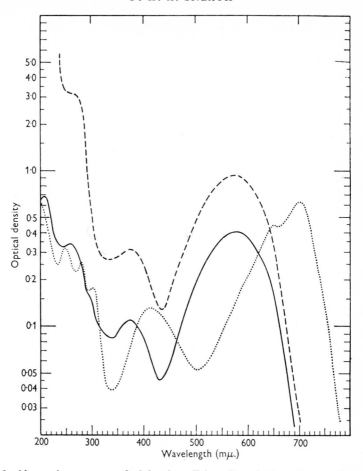

FIG. 1. Absorption spectra of violacein.—Ethanolic solution of crystalline violacein; .... crystalline violacein in 10% (v/v) sulphuric acid in 96% ethanol: - - -
crude violacein in ethanol. (Reproduced from Sneath 1956a, by permission of the
Journal of General Microbiology.)

(i) First check that the pigment does not diffuse away from the violet
colonies on agar plates (slight diffusion is seen in old cultures). (ii) Stir a
loopful of pigmented growth in chloroform and confirm that the pigment is
insoluble. (iii) Stir a loopful of growth in 96% ethyl alcohol in a hollowed
white tile, and check that it gives a violet solution. (iv) Transfer a loopful of
solution to a drop of dilute (25% v/v) sulphuric acid (turns green). (v) Add
10% (w/v) NaOH to the rest (turns green and then reddish). These reactions
are not given by other bacterial pigment as far as is known.

Flagella

Most strains of *Chromobacterium* in young agar cultures have an unusual form of flagellation: many cells have both polar and lateral (peritrichous) flagella. These are distinguishable in several ways in good flagellar-stained preparations:

Site of insertion. While the single polar flagellum is always inserted at the tip, the peritrichate flagella (often as many as 3 to 6) may be inserted anywhere on the cell—most often on the "shoulder" (sub-polar flagella).

Shape and staining. The polar flagellum usually shows long, shallow waves, and often stains faintly. The peritrichate (lateral) flagella usually show deep, short waves; they stain well, and are often very long in total length.

The two forms of flagella are also antigenically different. Old cultures, and cultures in liquid media, show few lateral flagella. Occasional strains never show lateral flagella.

Peroxide sensitivity

Not enough is yet known of the distribution of peroxide sensitivity, nor of the best techniques for testing it, to make this useful.

Tests for Distinguishing
Chromobacterium violaceum from *C. lividum*

Chromobacterium violaceum is mesophilic and strongly proteolytic. It is usually fermentative on a few carbohydrates, and is a facultative anaerobe.

C. lividum is psychrophilic and weakly proteolytic. It is a strict aerobe and attacks many carbohydrates oxidatively.

In the earlier literature these two species are much confused, and both have been commonly called *C. violaceum*. This name is now kept for the mesophilic group (Judicial Commission, 1958). The most convenient tests for distinguishing them are given below. It should be emphasized that occasional exceptions are found to all tests, but that it is very uncommon to find intermediate strains, i.e. strains which react atypically in several of them at once.

(a) Growth temperature

Growth temperature is tested on nutrient agar slants incubated at 37°C or at 4°C for 7 days after an inoculum of one drop of a broth culture.

(b) Hydrogen cyanide production

Production of HCN is conveniently tested for in stab cultures of semisolid

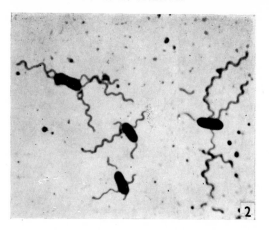

Fig. 2. Flagella-stained preparation of *C. violaceum* showing organisms with both polar and lateral flagella. × 2250. (Reproduced from Sneath 1956*b*, by permission of the *Journal of General Microbiology*.)

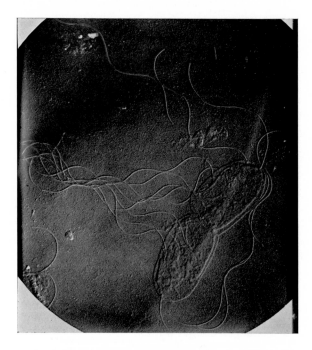

Fig. 3. Electron micrograph of *C. violaceum*, showing both polar and lateral flagella × 12,000. (Reproduced from Sneath 1956*b*, by permission of the *Journal of General Microbiology*.)

medium (nutrient agar diluted with an equal volume of water). An indicator paper is placed between tube and plug: it turns from yellow to brick red in 1–2 days at 25° if the cultures produce hydrogen cyanide (some pseudomonads are also positive in this test). The papers are made as follows: filter paper is dipped in saturated aqueous picric acid and dried, and then dipped in 10% aqueous sodium carbonate and again dried. They keep well.

(c) Acid from trehalose in Hugh and Leifson medium

Strains of *C. violaceum* are not invariably fermentative with glucose, though *C. lividum* is never strongly fermentative. A better distinction is given by 1% trehalose in the medium of Hugh and Leifson (1953), i.e. agar 0·3 g, peptone 0·2 g, NaCl 0·5 g, K_2HPO_4 0·3 g, bromthymol blue 0·003 g, and trehalose 1 g, water 100 ml. Adjust to pH 7·1, autoclave in tubes to a depth of 4 cm. Inoculate by stabbing and incubate at 25° for 4 days without a vaseline seal.

(d) Acid from arabinose in Hugh and Leifson medium

As (c) above with 1% arabinose instead of the trehalose; incubate for 7 days, as the attack may be slow.

(e) Aesculin hydrolysis

1% peptone, 0·1% sodium citrate, 0·1% aesculin, 0·005% ferric citrate, pH 7·0 in 5 ml quantities in tubes (a less toxic formulation than the earlier one in Sneath, 1960, p. 376). Incubate for 3–4 days at 25°.

(f) Casein hydrolysis

Plates of 50% skim milk with 1·5% agar added are streak inoculated and incubated for 4 days at 25°.

Results of the differential tests are shown in Table 1.

TABLE 1. Differential features of species of *Chromobacterium*

Test	C. violaceum	C. lividum
Growth at 37° in 7 days	Abundant	None or very slight
Growth at 4° in 7 days	None	Moderate
Hydrogen cyanide production	Positive	Negative
Trehalose	Acid (prompt)	No change or alkali
Arabinose	No change or alkali	Acid (often slow)
Aesculin hydrolysis	Negative	Positive (brown)
Casein hydrolysis	Positive (clear zone)	Negative or slight

References

HUGH, R., & LEIFSON, E. (1953). The taxonomic significance of fermentative versus oxidative metabolism of carbohydrates by various gram negative bacteria. *J. Bact.*, **66**, 24.

JUDICIAL COMMISSION (1958). *Opinion 16. Internat. Bull. bact. Nomencl. Taxon*, **8**, 151.

LEIFSON, E. (1956). Morphological and physiological characteristics of the genus *Chromobacterium*. *J. Bact.*, **71**, 393.

SNEATH, P. H. A. (1956a). Cultural and biochemical characteristics of the genus *Chromobacterium*. *J. gen. Microbiol.*, **15**, 70.

SNEATH, P. H. A. (1956b). The change from polar to peritrichous flagellation in *Chromobacterium* spp. *J. gen. Microbiol.*, **15**, 99.

SNEATH, P. H. A. (1960). A study of the bacterial genus *Chromobacterium*. *Iowa State J. Sci.*, **34**, 243.

Biochemical Identification of Enterobacteriaceae

K. Patricia Carpenter, S. P. Lapage
AND THE LATE K. J. Steel

Central Public Health Laboratory, Colindale, London, N.W.9, England

Though serological methods are of great importance in the routine identification of the major pathogenic groups of the Enterobacteriaceae, only biochemical methods are given here. Isolation techniques are omitted.

Methods

Biochemical tests and media

The temperature of incubation is 37° unless otherwise stated. In all the media Evans peptone has been substituted for other peptones described in the original formulae.

Fermentation tests. Carbohydrates 0·5% (w/v) in 1% (w/v) peptone water with Andrade indicator are used and the reactions observed daily.

H_2S production. This is detected by lead acetate papers inserted over nutrient broth or Gillies (1956) medium.

Indole. 2% (w/v) peptone water cultures, after incubation for 24 h, are tested with Kovacs' (1928) reagent; alternatively, Gillies (1956) indole test papers over Gillies (1956) medium may be used.

Urease. Christensen (1946) or Gillies (1956) medium is used.

Phenylpyruvic acid (PPA). The production of PPA from phenylalanine is detected (1) by the method of Henriksen (1950); (2) in the medium of Shaw and Clarke (1955), which is also used for the malonate utilization test; (3) on phenylalanine agar (Test 18, Report, 1958).

Methyl red (MR) and Voges-Proskauer (VP). Cultures grown in buffered glucose phosphate broth are tested after incubation for 3 days at 30° or 2 days at 37°. The VP test of O'Meara (1931) is used.

Citrate utilization. The medium of Simmons (1926) is used.

Malonate test. The medium and method is that of Shaw and Clarke (1955). This medium is also used for the PPA test.

Gluconate test. The method of Shaw and Clarke (1955) is used but modified (Carpenter, 1961) by substituting "Clinitest" Reagent Tablets (Ames

Company, Nuffield House, London, W.1) for Benedict qualitative solution.

Growth in KCN. The method of Møller (1954) is used, modified by using bijou bottles with caps very tightly screwed. Positive and negative controls are always used.

Gelatin liquefaction. Nutrient gelatin stab cultures are grown at room temperature and observed daily; alternatively, they are incubated at 37° and observed daily after cooling to about 18°.

Decarboxylases. The method of Møller (1955) is used.

Beta-galactosidase (ONPG) test. The test used is that of Lowe (1962) and further studied by Lapage and Jayaraman (1964).

Medium. (1) ONPG solution: orthonitrophenyl-β-D-galactopyranoside, 0·6 g; 0·01 M sodium phosphate (Na_2HPO_4) buffer at pH 7·5, 100 ml. Dissolve at room temperature and sterilize by Seitz filtration. (2) Add aseptically 1 part of ONPG solution to 3 parts of 1% (w/v) peptone water at pH 7·5. Distribute aseptically in 2 ml amounts. Incubate overnight at 37° to check sterility. The medium keeps for a month at 4°.

Test. Inoculate a tube of medium and incubate at 37°. A positive reaction is indicated by the formation of a yellow colour (orthonitrophenol). The colour change occurs in a few hours if the inoculum is heavy. Alternatively the tube can be inoculated lightly and incubated overnight. Longer incubation may give false positive results.

5% *Lactose.* The medium of Lowe and Evans (1957) is used.

Tartrates, mucate and sodium citrate tests. These are the tests described in Kauffmann (1961).

Nitrate reduction. Cultures in 0·1% (w/v) nitrate broth are tested, after incubation for 5 days, by the Griess-Ilosvay method (Wilson and Miles, 1964).

Oxidation/fermentation test. The medium is that of Hugh and Leifson (1953).

Oxidase. The method of Kovacs (1956) is used. The reagent is either 1% (w/v) p-aminodimethylaniline oxalate (Difco) or tetramethyl-p-phenylenediamine hydrochloride in distilled water. A platinum wire must be used for this test.

Gillies (1956) *medium.* This is a two-tube composite medium giving results for the tests in Table 2.

Biochemical Reactions of the Genera

Key to tables

A or $+$ = acid production from carbohydrate fermentation or positive reaction in other tests after overnight incubation.

$[+]$ = acid production or positive reaction after incubation for 48 h or longer.

G   = gas, $\frac{1}{4}$ or more volume of Durham tube; g = gas less than $\frac{1}{4}$ volume of Durham tube. Gas production recorded for glucose only.

D   = different species or serotypes give different reactions.

d   = different strains give different reactions.

$+/-$ or $-/+$ = reaction after oblique is a rare finding.

The reactions shown in the tables are those given by a majority of strains. Inevitably there are exceptions.

TABLE 1. Definition of family, Enterobacteriaceae

Gram-negative rods: non-acid-fast: non-sporing

Aerobes and facultative anaerobes

Show fermentative metabolism of glucose in Hugh and Leifson (1953) medium

May or may not produce gas from carbohydrate fermentation

Reduce nitrates to nitrites

Oxidase negative

Grow on ordinary and bile salt media

Normal habitat is the intestinal tract

TABLE 2. Screening reactions in Gillies (1956) medium

	Gillies tube I				§ Sucrose/salicin	Gillies tube II			(Additional test) Dulcitol
	Acid from glucose	Gas from glucose	Mannitol	*Urease		H₂S	Indole	Motility	
Shigella sonnei	+	—	+	—	—	—	—	—	—
Other Shigella sp.	+	−/+	D	—	—	—	d	—	D
‡Escherichia	+	+	+	—	d	—	+	+	d
Typical Salmonella sp.	+	+	+	—	—	+	—	+	+
Salmonella typhi	+	—	+	—	—	+	—	+	—
Arizona	+	+	+	—	—	+	—	+	—
Citrobacter	+	+	+	—	d	+	−/+	+	d
†Klebsiella	+	+	+	+ (weak)	+	—	−/+	—	d
†‡Hafnia/Enterobacter/Serratia	+	+	+	d (weak)	d	—	—	+	—
Proteus	unreadable		−/+	+	D	D	D	+	—
‡Providencia	+	−/+	−/+	—	d	—	+	+	—

* A positive urease reaction masks fermentation of glucose and mannitol.
† A weak alkali or weak urease production in these genera may mask the fermentation of mannitol and sometimes glucose.
‡ These genera are frequently non-motile if tested immediately after isolation.
§ It is impossible to determine in this medium which carbohydrate is fermented.

TABLE 3. Fermentation reactions of genera*

Genera	Glucose	Lactose	Mannitol	Sucrose	Dulcitol	Salicin	Xylose	Adonitol	Inositol
Shigella	A	–	D	–	D	–	D	–	–
Escherichia	AG	+/–	+	d	d	d	+	–	–
Salmonella	AG/A	–	+	–	+	–	+	–	d
Arizona	AG	+/–	+	d	–	–	+	–	–
Citrobacter	AG	+/–	+	d	d	d	+	–	–
Klebsiella	AG	+	+	+	d	+	+	+	+
Hafnia	AG	–	+	d	–	d	+	–	–
Enterobacter	AG	d	+	d	d	+	+	d	D
Serratia	Ag	–	+	+	–	d	d	d	d
Proteus	AG/A	–	D	d	–	d	D	D	D
Providencia	A/Ag	–	–/+	d	–	d	–	d	d

* After incubation for 24 h.
See detailed tables for species differentiation.

TABLE 4. Other biochemical reactions of genera

Genera	Urease	PPA	MR	VP	Citrate	Malo-nate	Gluco-nate	KCN	β-galacto-sidase	5% lactose	Decarboxylases			Gelatin
											Argi-nine	Lysine	Orni-thine	
Shigella	−	−	+	−	−	−	−	−	−/+	−/[+]	−/[+]	−	D	−
Escherichia	−	−	+	−	−	−	−	−	+	+	d	d	d	−
Salmonella	−	−	+	−	+	−/+	−	−	−	−	[+]*	+	+	−/[+]
Arizona	−	−	+	−	+	+	−	−	+	+/−	[+]*	+	+	[+]
Citrobacter	−/+	−	+	−	+	d	−	+	+/−	+/−	+/[+]	−	−/+	−
Klebsiella	+	−	D	D	+	D	D	D	+	+	−	+	−	−
†*Hafnia*	d	−	−	+	+	+/−	+	+	+	−	−	+	+	+
Enterobacter	d	−	−	+	+	d	+	+	+	+	D	D	+	[+]/−
Serratia	−	−	−/+	−/+	+	−	+	+	+	−	−	+	+	+
Proteus	+	+	+/−	D	D	−	−/+	+	−	−	−	−	D	D
Providencia	−	+	+	−	+	−	−	+	−	−	−	−	−	−

* Characteristically positive after incubation for 48 h.
† MR, VP and citrate reactions are those given after incubation at 30°. Some strains may be MR +, VP −, citrate −, if incubated at 37°.

TABLE 5. Classification and nomenclature of *Shigella*

Subgroup	Name	Characters	Serotypes
A	*Sh. dysenteriae*	Non-mannitol-fermenters: each member serologically distinct	1–10
B	*Sh. flexneri*	Mannitol-fermenters with exceptions*: members serologically related to each other	1–6, X and Y
C	*Sh. boydii*	Mannitol-fermenters: each member serologically distinct	1–15
D	*Sh. sonnei*	Mannitol-fermenter: late lactose and sucrose fermenter: contains only one member: serologically distinct	—

* Exceptions are the biotype of *Sh. flexneri* 4a, sometimes known as *Sh. rabaulensis*, and the Newcastle biotype of *Sh. flexneri* 6.
Non-mannitol-fermenting strains of usually mannitol-fermenting subgroups may occur.

TABLE 6. Diagnostic biochemical reactions of *Shigella* subgroups

	Sh. dysenteriae	*Sh. flexneri**	*Sh. boydii**	*Sh. sonnei*
Glucose	A	A	A	A
Lactose	—	—	—	[+]
Mannitol	—	+	+	+
Sucrose	—	—	—	[+]
Dulcitol	—/+	—	D	—
Xylose	—/+	—	d	—/+
Indole	D	d	D	—
Ornithine decarboxylase	—	—	—/+	+

All subgroups: non-motile, H_2S—, urease—, PPA—, citrate—, KCN—, malonate—, gluconate—, do not liquefy gelatin, do not ferment salicin, adonitol or inositol.

* Only certain biotypes of *Sh. flexneri* 6 (Table 7) and *Sh. boydii* 14 (Carpenter, 1961) are aerogenic.
Dulcitol: *Sh. dysenteriae* 5 and *Sh. boydii* 2, 3, 4 and 6 give a positive reaction.
Indole: *Sh. dysenteriae* 1, *Sh. flexneri* 6 and *Sh. sonnei* invariably give a negative reaction. *Sh. dysenteriae* 2 invariably gives a positive reaction.

TABLE 7. Biotypes of *Shigella flexneri* 6*

Old names	Glucose	Mannitol	Dulcitol†	Indole
Boyd type 88	A	A	—	—
Boyd type 88	A	A	A	—
Sh. newcastle	AG/A	—	AG/A/—	—
Manchester bacillus	AG	AG	AG/—	—

* All biotypes are serologically identical.
† Fermentation of this may be delayed.

Some characters of the genus Salmonella

Motile with peritrichous flagella, non-motile flagellate or non-flagellate strains may occur; two species, *Salmonella gallinarum* and *S. pullorum* are non-flagellate. Some salmonellae possess fimbriae.

Metabolism. Salmonellae show a mixed acid fermentation, the methyl red test is positive and acetyl-methyl-carbinol is not produced. Indole is not formed, nor is urea hydrolysed. Glucose is fermented with the production of acid, and gas is produced by most strains, except members of the species *S. typhi* and *S. gallinarum*. Mannitol is fermented. Maltose is fermented by the majority of species, but for a few, e.g. *S. pullorum*, the absence of maltose fermentation is characteristic. Dulcitol is fermented by most species, but a few medically important species attack it late or do not ferment it, e.g. *S. paratyphi A*, *S. typhi*, *S. cholerae-suis*. Lactose, sucrose and adonitol are not fermented. Occasional biochemically aberrant strains occur, but the vast majority yield the typical reactions given above.

In some species a serotype may be divided into biotypes by various biochemical reactions, e.g. *S. cholerae-suis*, *S. enteritidis*.

TABLE 8. Biochemical reactions of *Salmonella* subgenera

(Modified from Kauffmann, 1964*a*,
and atypical subgenus II modified from Kauffmann, 1964*b*)

Tests	Subgenus			
	I	II	Atypical II	III = *Arizona*
0·5% Lactose	—	—	—	+ or [+] or —
β-galactosidase	—	−/[+]	—	+
Dulcitol	+	+	—	—
Gelatin	—	[+]	—	[+]
D-tartrate	+	− or [+]	− or [+]	− or [+]
L-tartrate	d	—	—	—
I-tartrate	d	—	—	—
Sodium citrate	+	+	+	+
Mucate	+	+	—	d
Malonate	—	+	—	—

TABLE 9. Differentiation of certain biotypes of *Salmonella* and *Shigella*

Tests	Typical *Salmonella* sp.	Anaerogenic *Salmonella* strain*	*S. typhi*†	*Shigella sonnei*	*Sh. flexneri* 6 (Manchester var.)
Gas from glucose	+	−	−	−	+
Dulcitol	+	+	−/[+]	−	d
Xylose	+	+	d	−/+	−
Arabinose	+	+	d	+	+
H₂S	+	+	d	−	−
Motility	+	+	+	−	−
Decarboxylases:					
Lysine	+	+	+	−	−
Ornithine	+	+	−	+	−

* The poultry strains *Salmonella pullorum* and *gallinarum* are excluded from this table.
† The majority of strains received at the Salmonella Reference Laboratory produce H₂S in one day.

TABLE 10. Diagnostic biochemical reactions of the genus *Klebsiella* (Cowan *et al.*, 1960, modified by Steel)

	K. aerogenes	*K. pneumoniae*	*K. edwardsii* var. *edwardsii*	*K. edwardsii* var. *atlantae*	*K. rhino-scleromatis*	*K. ozaenae*
Gas from glucose	+	+	−	+	−	d
Lactose	+	+	[+]	[+]	−	[+]
Dulcitol	d	+	−	−	−	−
MR	−	+	d	+	+	+
VP	+	−	+	d	−	−
Citrate	+	+	d	+	−	d
Urease	+	+	+	+	−	d
KCN	+	−	+	+	+	+
Malonate	+	+	d	−	+	−
Gluconate	+	d	+	d	−	−
Lysine decarboxylase	+	+	+	+	−	d

TABLE 11. Differentiation of *Klebsiella*, *Hafnia* and *Enterobacter*

Tests	Klebsiella	Hafnia	Enterobacter cloacae	Enterobacter aerogenes
Motility	−	+	+	+
Adonitol	+	−	d	+
Inositol	+	−	−	+
Gelatin	−	−	[+]/−	d*
Decarboxylases:				
Arginine	−	−	+	−
Lysine	+	+	−	+
Ornithine	−	+	+	+

* If positive, liquefaction is delayed.

TABLE 12. Diagnostic biochemical reactions of *Proteus-Providence* group*
(Carpenter, 1964)

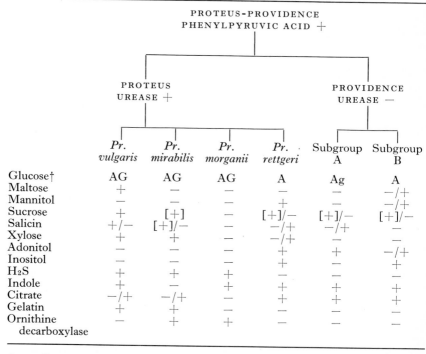

PROTEUS-PROVIDENCE
PHENYLPYRUVIC ACID +

PROTEUS
UREASE +

PROVIDENCE
UREASE −

	Pr. vulgaris	Pr. mirabilis	Pr. morganii	Pr. rettgeri	Subgroup A	Subgroup B
Glucose†	AG	AG	AG	A	Ag	A
Maltose	+	−	−	−	−	−/+
Mannitol	−	−	−	+	−	−/+
Sucrose	+	[+]	−	[+]/−	[+]/−	[+]/−
Salicin	+/−	[+]/−	−	−/+	−/+	−
Xylose	+	+	−	−/+	−	−
Adonitol	−	−	−	+	+	−/+
Inositol	−	−	−	+	−	+
H₂S	+	+	+	−	−	−
Indole	+	−	+	+	+	+
Citrate	−/+	−/+	−	+	+	+
Gelatin	+	+	−	−	−	−
Ornithine decarboxylase	−	+	+	−	−	−

Anomalies: anaerogenic strains of *Pr. vulgaris*, *mirabilis* and *morganii* and aerogenic strains of *Pr. rettgeri* occur occasionally. Some *Pr. vulgaris* strains are indole negative and some *Pr. mirabilis* strains are indole positive.
* Reproduced from *Recent Advances in Clinical Pathology*, Series IV, by kind permission of the publishers, Messrs J. & A. Churchill Ltd, London.
† Gas production is recorded from glucose only.

TABLE 13. The β-galactosidase (ONPG) test compared to lactose fermentation
(Modified from Lapage and Jayaraman, 1964)

Tests	Pattern of results					
ONPG	+	+	+	+	+	+
5% lactose	+	+	+	+	+	−
1% lactose	+	+	[+] or −	[+] or −	−	−
MacConkey agar†	+	−	[+] or −	[+] or −	−	−

No. of strains giving these reactions:

Strains of Enterobacteriaceae* Classified as	Total No.						
Escherichia	82	60	4	10	8	0	0
Citrobacter	36	12	2	15	5	0	2
Klebsiella	41	39	0	2	0	0	0
Enterobacter/Hafnia/Serratia	62	11	4	31	4	12	0
Unclassifiable	15	5	1	2	2	1	4

* Wild strains from human sources.
† Lactose-fermenting colony = +; non-lactose-fermenting colony = −.

References

CARPENTER, K. P. (1961). The relation of the Enterobacterium A12 (Sachs) to *Shigella boydii* 14. *J. gen. Microbiol.*, **26**, 535.

CARPENTER, K. P. (1964). The Proteus-Providence Group. In *Recent Advances in Clinical Pathology*, Ser. IV, p. 13. Ed. S. C. Dyke. London: Churchill.

CHRISTENSEN, W. B. (1946). Urea decomposition as a means of differentiating *Proteus* and paracolon cultures from each other and from *Salmonella* and *Shigella* types. *J. Bact.*, **52**, 461.

COWAN, S. T., STEEL, K. J., SHAW, C., & DUGUID, J. P. (1960). A classification of the *Klebsiella* group. *J. gen. Microbiol.*, **23**, 601.

GILLIES, R. R. (1956). An evaluation of two composite media for preliminary identification of *Shigella* and *Salmonella*. *J. clin. Path.*, **9**, 368.

HENRIKSEN, S. D. (1950). A comparison of the phenylpyruvic acid reaction and the urease test in the differentiation of *Proteus* from other enteric organisms. *J. Bact.*, **60**, 225.

HUGH, R., & LEIFSON, E. (1953). The taxonomic significance of fermentative versus oxidative metabolism of carbohydrates by various Gram-negative bacteria. *J. Bact.*, **66**, 24.

KAUFFMANN, F. (1961). *Die Bakteriologie der Salmonella species*. Copenhagen: Munksgaard.

KAUFFMANN, F. (1964a). Das Kauffmann-White-Schema. In *The World Problem of Salmonellosis* (*Monographiae Biologicae* **13**), p. 21. Ed. E. Van Oye. The Hague: Junk.

KAUFFMANN, F. (1964b). Weitere *Salmonella* species des Subgenus II in 1963. *Acta path. microbiol. scand.*, **61**, 579.

KOVACS, N. (1928). Eine vereinfachte Methode zum Nachweis der Indolbildung durch Bakterien. *Z. ImmunForsch.*, **55**, 311.

KOVACS, N. (1956). Identification of *Pseudomonas pyocyanea* by the oxidase reaction. *Nature, Lond.*, **128**, 703.

LAPAGE, S. P., & JAYARAMAN, M. S. (1964). Beta-galactosidase and lactose fermentation in the identification of enterobacteria including salmonellae. *J. clin. Path.*, **17**, 117.

LOWE, G. H. (1962). The rapid detection of lactose fermentation in paracolon organisms by the demonstration of Beta-D-galactosidase. *J. med. lab. Technol.*, **19**, 21.

LOWE, G. H., & EVANS, J. H. (1957). A simple medium for the rapid detection of salmonella-like paracolon organisms. *J. clin. Path.*, **10**, 318.

MØLLER, V. (1954). Diagnostic use of the Braun KCN test within the Enterobacteriaceae. *Acta path. microbiol. scand.*, **34**, 115.

MØLLER, V. (1955). Simplified tests for some amino acid decarboxylases and for the arginine dihydrolase system. *Acta path. microbiol. scand.*, **36**, 158.

O'MEARA, R. A. Q. (1931). A simple delicate and rapid method of detecting the formation of acetylmethylcarbinol by bacteria fermenting carbohydrate. *J. Path. Bact.*, **34**, 401.

REPORT (1958). Report of the Enterobacteriaceae Subcommittee of the Nomenclature Committee of the International Association of Microbiological Societies. *Int. Bull. bact. Nomencl.*, **8**, 25.

SHAW, C., & CLARKE, P. H. (1955). Biochemical classification of *Proteus* and Providence cultures. *J. gen. Microbiol.* **13**, 155.

SIMMONS, J. S. (1926). A culture medium for differentiating organisms of typhoid-colon aerogenes groups and for isolation of certain fungi. *J. infect. Dis.*, **39**, 209.

WILSON, G. S., & MILES, A. A. (1964). *Topley & Wilson's Principles of Bacteriology and Immunity*, 5th ed. London: Arnold.

General references (not included in text) to Enterobacteriaceae

EDWARDS, P. R., & EWING, W. H. (1962). *Identification of Enterobacteriaceae.* Minneapolis: Burgess Publishing Co.

KAUFFMANN, F. (1954). *Enterobacteriaceae*, 2nd ed. Copenhagen: Munksgaard.

REPORT (1963). Report of the Enterobacteriaceae Subcommittee of the Nomenclature Committee of the International Association of Microbiological Societies —1962. *Int. Bull. bact. Nomencl.*, **13**, 69.

SEDLAK, J., & RISCHE, H. (1961). *Enterobacteriaceae-Infektionen.* Leipzig: Thieme.

Techniques in the Identification and Classification of *Brucella*

W. J. Brinley Morgan and S. G. M. Gower

Ministry of Agriculture, Fisheries and Food,
Central Veterinary Laboratory, Weybridge, Surrey, England

The genus *Brucella* has been divided into three species—*Brucella melitensis,* *B. abortus* and *B. suis,* as shown in Table 1.

TABLE 1. Conventional methods for separating species in the genus *Brucella*

Species	Need for added CO_2 for growth	H_2S production	Growth on medium containing		Agglutination in monospecific antisera	
			basic fuchsin	thionin	abortus	melitensis
B. melitensis	—	—	+	+	—	+
B. abortus	+	Moderate, 4 days	+	—	+	—
B. suis	—	Heavy, 5 days	—	+	+	—

+ positive reaction
— negative reaction

This scheme, based on the work of Huddleson (1929), and Wilson and Miles (1932) also fitted in well with the host reservoirs of the species, but over the years several cultures have been found which differed in some characteristics from those species listed above. These are included in Table 2. (See reviews by Huddleson, 1943, 1961; Biberstein and Cameron, 1961; Morgan, 1964; Renoux, 1958; Stableforth, 1959; Stableforth and Jones, 1963).

By the use of Brucella bacteriophage Tbilisi (Tb, originally isolated in the Soviet Union) at 2 dilutions, viz. Routine Test Dilution (RTD) and 10,000 × RTD, it has been shown that cultures of *B. abortus* were lysed by both dilutions, *B. melitensis* by neither and *B. suis* showed no lysis at RTD, but showed lysis at 10,000 × RTD (Morgan, 1963). This effect can still be seen after partial purification of the phage (Table 3).

TABLE 2. The classification of Brucella

Old designation Species/type	New designation Species	Biotype	CO_2 req.	H_2S prod.	Growth on media with basic fuchsin	Growth on media with thionin	Agglutination in monospecific antisera abortus	Agglutination in monospecific antisera melitensis	Lysis by phage Tb. RTD	Lysis by phage Tb. 10,000 × RTD	Oxidative metabolic test Glutamic acid	Oxidative metabolic test Ornithine	Oxidative metabolic test Ribose	Oxidative metabolic test Lysine
B. abortus	B. abortus	1	++	++	+	—	++	—	L	L	++	—	++	—
B. abortus Wilson type II		2	++	++	—	—	++	—	L	L	++	—	++	—
B. abortus thionin resistant		3	(+)	+	+	+	+	—	L	L	+	—	+	—
B. abortus/melitensis		4	(+)	+	++++	—	—	++	L	L	++++	—	+++	—
British melitensis		5	—	—	++++	+++	—	++	L	L	++++	—	+++	—
B. intermedia		6	—	—	+++++	++++	++	—	L	L	+++++	—	++	—
B. melitensis—more "a"		7	—	(+)	+++++	+++++	—	+	L	L	+++++	—	++	—
CO₂ req. melitensis		8	+	—	+++++	+++++	—	—	L	NL	+++++	—	—	—
H₂S prod. melitensis		9	—	+	+++++	+++++	++	+	L	NL	+++++	—	—	—
B. melitensis	B. melitensis	1	—	—	—	++++	—	+++	NL	NL	+++	—	—	—
B. intermedia		2	—	—	—	+++	—	+	NL	L	+++	—	—	—
B. melitensis—more "a"		3	—	—	(—)	++++	++	+	NL	L	+++	—	—	—
B. suis	B. suis	1	—	++	++++	++++	++++	—	NL	L	+++	+++	+++	+
B. suis Danish		2	—	—	—	++	++	—	NL	L	+++	+++	+++	—
American melitensis		3	—	—	+	++	—	+	NL	L	+++	+++	+++	++
B. rangiferi tarandi	B. rangiferi tarandi		—	—	(—)	+	++	—	NL	L	+	+++	+++	+
B. ovis	B. ovis		+	—	—	+	—	—	NL	NL	+	—	—	—

NL = not lysed.
L = lysed.

++ = positive.
++ = strongly positive (H_2S test only).
(+) = usually positive.

(—) = usually negative.
— = negative.

TABLE 3. The lytic effect of partially purified phage Tb

Phage preparation (pfp = plaque-forming particles)	Species			
	B. meli-tensis 16M	*B. abortus* 544	*B. suis* 1330	*B. suis* 20 other cultures
Phage Tb undiluted stock preparation (2·5 × 10¹¹ pfp/ml)	N.L.	C.L.	C.L.	C.L.
Phage Tb at RTD (20 × 10⁶ pfp/ml)	N.L.	C.L.	N.L.	N.L.
Phage Tb partially purified by 2 centrifugations at 100,000**g** for 1 h (6·5 × 10¹¹ pfp/ml)	N.L.	C.L.	C.L.	C.L.
Phage Tb partially purified RTD (25 × 10⁶ pfp/ml)	N.L.	C.L.	N.L.	N.L.
Supernatant of phage Tb collected after centrifugation at 100,000**g** for 1 h (45 × 10⁸ pfp/ml)	N.L.	C.L.	N.L.	—

C.L. = complete lysis. N.L. = no lysis. — = test not done

By using a series of amino acids and carbohydrates as substrates, it was shown by Meyer and Cameron (1961*a*, *b*) that type I of each of the species *B. melitensis*, *B. abortus* and *B. suis* (determined by conventional typing methods, Table 1) had a characteristic metabolic pattern and that cultures which were atypical by conventional typing methods had the metabolic pattern of one or other of the three species. It was further shown (Meyer, 1961, Meyer and Morgan, 1962) that all cultures with the metabolic pattern of *B. abortus*, irrespective of their properties as determined by conventional methods, were lysed by Brucella phages at RTD; cultures with the oxidative metabolic pattern of *B. melitensis* were not lysed (see Table 2).

Species Designation

At the 7th International Congress for Microbiology (Stockholm, 1958), a Subcommittee on Taxonomy of *Brucella* was appointed to study the question of species designation in this genus. In its report (Stableforth and Jones, 1963) the Subcommittee recommended the retention of the three species—*B. melitensis*, *B. abortus* and *B. suis*—speciation being confirmed by oxidative metabolism and phage susceptibility tests. A number of biotypes within each species was also proposed, biotype differentiation being confirmed by the use of the conventional typing methods.

The genus and the three species of *Brucella* were defined as follows:

Brucella: Small, non-motile, non-sporing, Gram-negative coccobacilli. Grow rather poorly on ordinary media or may require special media. Aerobic, no growth under strict anaerobic conditions. Growth often improved by CO_2. Little fermentative action on carbohydrates in usual media. Urea hydrolysed to a variable extent. Parasites occurring in animals and producing characteristic infections in animals and man.

Brucella melitensis: Aerobic. Produce no H_2S or no more than a trace on ordinary media. Usually grow in the presence of basic fuchsin and thionin. Usually have M antigen predominant. Oxidize L-alanine, D-alanine, L-asparagine and L-glutamic acid. Do not oxidize L-arabinose, D-galactose, D-ribose, D-xylose, L-arginine, DL-citrulline, DL-ornithine or L-lysine. Not lysed by Brucella phage Tb (Tbilisi) at routine test dilution. Usually pathogenic for goats and sheep, but can also affect other species, including cattle and man.

Reference strain, *B. melitensis* 16M.

Brucella abortus: Usually require added CO_2 for growth, especially on primary isolation. Usually produce moderate amounts of H_2S, but sometimes none. Usually grow in presence of basic fuchsin, but inhibited by thionin. Usually have A antigen predominant. Oxidize L-alanine, D-alanine, L-asparagine, L-glutamic acid, L-arabinose, D-galactose and D-ribose; do not oxidize D-xylose, L-arginine, DL-citrulline, DL-ornithine or L-lysine. Cultures in the smooth or smooth-intermediate phase are lysed by Brucella phage Tb (Tbilisi) at routine test dilution. Usually pathogenic for cattle causing abortion, but can also affect other species including man.

Reference strain, *B. abortus* 544.

Brucella suis: Aerobic. Produce large amounts of H_2S or none at all. Grow in the presence of thionin, but usually inhibited by basic fuchsin. Usually have A antigen predominant. Oxidize L-alanine, D-alanine, L-glutamic acid, L-arabinose, D-galactose, D-ribose, D-xylose, L-arginine, DL-citrulline, DL-ornithine and L-lysine. Do not oxidize L-asparagine. Not lysed by Brucella phage Tb (Tbilisi) at routine test dilution. Usually pathogenic for pigs, but can also affect hares and other species including man.

Reference strain, *B. suis* 1330.

Other species

B. *neotomae* (Stoenner and Lackman, 1957). This was isolated from the desert wood rat (*Neotomae lepida*). In many respects it resembles B. *suis*, e.g. it is aerobic, it produces H_2S, it is inhibited by basic fuchsin, it grows on low levels of thionin, shows lysis by phage at 10,000 × RTD but not at RTD and is agglutinated by mono-specific abortus antiserum.

B. *ovis* (Buddle, 1956) is the aetiological agent of ram epididymitis. It has been regarded as a stable rough variant of B. *melitensis* and does not agglutinate in monospecific antisera and is not lysed by phage. In our laboratory many cultures of B. *ovis* isolated in different parts of the world have been examined for their oxidative metabolic pattern and they have all given a pattern similar to that of B. *melitensis*.

B. *rangiferi tarandi* (Davydov, 1961). These have been isolated from reindeer in the far north of Russia. Strains with similar properties have also been isolated from Eskimos and caribou in Alaska. These cultures are aerobic, do not produce H_2S, grow on thionin but tend to be inhibited by basic fuchsin. In the writers' laboratory cultures from both Russia and Alaska agglutinated in both monospecific antisera, showed lysis by phage at 10,000 × RTD, but not at RTD, and on oxidative metabolism tests gave patterns similar to those of B. *suis* biotype 3 (Table 2).

The exact taxonomic position of these "species" must await further study.

Vaccine strains

(a) B. *abortus* strain 19. This is widely used for vaccinating cattle. The strain is aerobic and of reduced virulence, but is otherwise similar to biotype 1 strain. There is no *single* character that can distinguish it from other strains of biotype 1, but there are a number of characters which, *collectively*, can be of value.

(1) *Thionin blye sensitivity*. The growth of strain 19 is inhibited by a concentration of thionin blue (1/500,000) which allows the growth of other strains of B. *abortus*. However, it has been found (Morgan, 1961) that there are three groups of B. *abortus* that do not grow in this concentration of the dye, viz:
   (i) Strains resembling strain 19.
   (ii) Strains of B. *arbortus* biotype 2.
   (iii) A previously undescribed group. Cultures of this group differ from strain 19 in that they require added CO_2 for growth and are virulent for guinea pigs.

(2) *Sensitivity to penicillin*.* The growth of strain 19 is inhibited by 10 I.U. of penicillin; field strains are not inhibited. The growth of

* Tested by applying sensitivity discs to surface growth on agar.

cultures of *B. abortus* biotype 2 is also inhibited by penicillin, completely by 10 I.U. and to a lesser extent by 5 I.U.

(3) *Virulence for guinea pigs.* This can be assessed in a number of ways, e.g.:

    (i) Estimating the $I.D._{50}$.

    (ii) Challenging with a standard challenge dose (e.g. 4×10^9 viable organisms) and estimating the number of organisms per gram of spleen at a given time (11 days) after challenge (Stableforth, 1959).

    (iii) Duration of bacteraemia following challenge with a large dose (18×10^9 cells) (Cruickshank, 1957).

The differential characters for strain 19 can therefore be summarized in Table 4.

TABLE 4. Differential characters of Strain 19

Culture	CO_2 for growth (1)	Growth on medium plus (2)					Lysis by phage at RTD (3)	Virulence for guinea pigs
		Basic fuch-sin	Thio-nin	Thio-nin blue	Penicillin 5 I.U.	Penicillin 10 I.U.		
B. abortus field strains	+	+	−	+	+	+	L	Virulent
B. abortus biotype 2	+	−	−	−	(−)	−	L	Virulent
Field strains, but thionin blue sensitive	+	+	−	−	+	+	L	Virulent
Strain 19	−	+	−	−	−	−	L	Low virulence

(1) + = added CO_2 needed for growth.
(2) + = growth, − no growth, (−) slight growth.
(3) L = culture lysed.

(b) *B. melitensis* Rev. 1. This is used for vaccinating goats. The strain is of reduced virulence for guinea pigs, goats and monkeys. It produces small colonies which do not exceed 1–2 mm diameter even after incubation for 4–5 days. Other cultures of *B. melitensis* produce larger colonies even after 2–3 days.

The growth of Rev. 1 in air is inhibited by 1/50,000 thionin and 1/50,000 basic fuchsin, although this is less well marked when plates are incubated in 10% CO_2, when growth occurs on the first two or three strokes.

The growth of Rev. 1 is inhibited by 5–10 I.U. of penicillin; other types of *B. melitensis* grow at this concentration.

Lastly, the growth of Rev. 1 is not inhibited by 5 μg/ml streptomycin, which inhibits the growth of other cultures of *B. melitensis*.

The differential characters of Rev. 1 are summarized in Table 5.

TABLE 5. Differential characters of Rev. 1

	Growth on medium containing				Colony size	Virulence
	Basic fuchsin	Thionin	Penicillin	Streptomycin		
B. melitensis	+	+	+	−	3–4 mm	Virulent
Rev. 1	(−)	(−)	−	+	maxm	Reduced
					1–2 mm	virulence

+ = growth; (−) = slight growth; − = no growth.

Laboratory Techniques

Brucellosis is one of the more readily acquired laboratory infections; most strains of *Brucella* are capable of causing disease in man and it is strongly recommended that the procedures described here should be done in a ventilated cabinet to reduce the risk of human infection. The following techniques are used at this laboratory for the identification and classification of *Brucella*.

1. Culture media

(a) The *basal medium* consists of 1% (w/v) Lemco beef extract, 1% (w/v) Oxoid peptone, 0·5% (w/v) NaCl, 1·5% (w/v) Agar, pH 7·5. Autoclaved at 10 lb/in² for 15 min.

(b) For the growth of cultures, and phage tests; to the basal medium is added 5% (v/v) Brucella negative bovine (or equine) serum and 1% (w/v) glucose, to give serum dextrose agar (SDA).

(c) For the propagation of phage; sloppy agar is used, i.e. the basal medium contains only 0·7% agar instead of 1·5%.

(d) For studying dissociation; glycerin dextrose agar (GDA) is used; i.e. to the basal medium, 2% glycerin and 1% glucose is added after autoclaving, from a stock solution of 50% (v/v) glycerin and 25% (w/v) glucose sterilized by seitz-filtration.

(e) For dye sensitivity tests; SDA is used, containing 1/25,000 basic fuchsin and 1/50,000 thionin (these dyes are obtained via the World Health Organization from the National Aniline Division, Allied Chemical and Dye Co, New York). Occasionally, thionin blue at 1/500,000 (British Drug Houses Ltd, London) is also incorporated. The dyes are made as

0·1% (w/v) stock solutions in distilled water and steamed for 1 h to sterilize, and are replaced every 3 months.

2. Dissociation studies

(a) *Direct observation using obliquely transmitted light* (Henry, 1933). This requires a microscope lamp with a blue filter, a stereoscopic microscope with a clear glass stage, capable of giving magnification of 15 to 25, and a concave mirror placed between the lamp and microscope (see Fig. 1). Ideally this should be set up in a box to reduce interference from incidental light.

Plates containing glycerin-dextrose agar are streaked with the culture so as to produce areas of dense growth as well as isolated colonies. It is important that the medium should be clear and of even depth. After 4 days of incubation, the growth is examined under the microscope. Smooth colonies of *B. abortus* are convex, 2 mm diam, with an entire

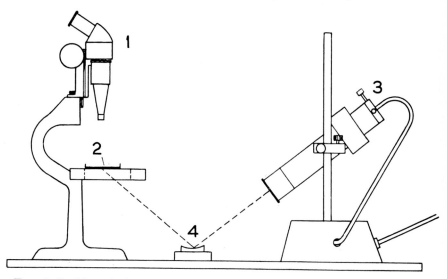

FIG. 1. Position of microscope and lamp for oblique-light observation of bacterial dissociation of Brucella. 1 = microscope (magnification × 15); 2 = glass stage with culture plate; 3 = lamp giving concentrated beam of light; 4 = mirror.

edge, and a blue, glistening and homogenous appearance. Rough colonies are yellow, opaque, granular and break up when touched with a needle. Intermediate colonies are the most difficult to classify and have an appearance intermediate between smooth and rough, i.e. are slightly more opaque and granular than the smooth colonies. Mucoid colonies are glistening, greyish in colour and have a slimy consistency when touched with a needle.

(b) *Agglutinability in acriflavine.* A 1/1000 solution of neutral acriflavine is used. The test is easily done by placing a drop of the acriflavine solution on a clean slide; a colony is touched with a straight wire and emulsified in the acriflavine. Smooth colonies emulsify easily to produce a homogenous suspension of cells undergoing Brownian movement. Rough colonies are difficult to emulsify and/or are agglutinated immediately; mucoid colonies form threads. Intermediate colonies behave like smooth colonies or may produce a fine, granular agglutination.

(c) *Staining of colonies with crystal violet* (White and Wilson, 1951). The stain is prepared as follows: Solution A, 2 g crystal violet in 20 ml of 95% alcohol; Solution B, 0·8 g ammonium oxalate in 80 ml of distilled water. The two solutions are mixed to form a stock solution which is then diluted 1/40 for use.

The plate is flooded with the stain and allowed to act for 15 to 20 sec, after which it is drained into disinfectant. Under the stereoscopic microscope, smooth colonies are pale yellow colour; rough colonies are red with a coarse, granular appearance; other dissociated colonies are stained various shades of purple and blue.

3. Monospecific antisera

Antisera for *B. abortus* and *B. melitensis* are prepared in rabbits, using heat-killed cells. The rabbits are bled every other day from the 5th to the 12th days and the sera collected and kept separately. The titre against homologous and heterologous antigens is determined for each lot of serum and the heterologous antibodies absorbed by the addition of heat-killed heterologous cells. The proportion of cells required is obtained by trial, using 1 ml of antiserum. After absorption, the appropriate antisera are pooled, and retested by the tube dilution method against both antigens. Full details are given by Jones (1958). As a routine, cultures are tested by the slide-agglutination method, using antisera diluted 1/5 in phenol-saline.

4. Production of hydrogen sulphide

Sheets of filter paper are soaked in a 10% (w/v) solution of lead acetate and hung up to dry in neutral air. When dry, the sheets are cut into strips and then autoclaved.

The culture is seeded on SDA slopes and a strip of lead-acetate paper is placed between the cotton-wool plug and glass and the culture incubated.

If H₂S is produced, the tip of the lead-acetate paper is blackened. The cultures are examined daily for 4 days, and, if H₂S has been produced, a fresh strip of lead-acetate paper is used (see Fig. 2).

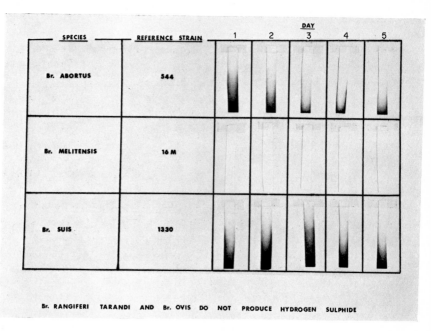

FIG. 2. Hydrogen sulphide production of the different Brucella species over a period of 5 days.

5. Phage sensitivity tests

The following phages are used: Tb, 212/XIV and 371/XXIX. *B. abortus* strain 544 is used as propagating strain for phage Tb and *B. abortus* strain 12 for the other two.

For the preparation of stock preparations with high titres, the double agar layer technique has been found to give best results.

The propagating culture is grown on SDA for 18 to 24 h and the growth suspended in peptone water and adjusted so as to contain *c* 10¹⁰ cells/ml. The semi-solid agar is melted and cooled to 44°C in a water bath, and 0·25 ml of the bacterial suspension added. Phage is added and the inoculated semi-solid agar is well mixed and poured over a plate containing serum dextrose agar on a level bench and incubated for 24 h. The amount of phage necessary to cause nearly complete lysis is titrated in a preliminary trial before making the main batch of phage.

The phage is then harvested by scraping off the semi-solid agar layer into peptone water, left overnight at 4°C and then centrifuged to deposit the agar and cells. The supernatant is collected, filtered through Oxoid millipore filters (0·8 μ diam.) and toluene added as a preservative to give a final concentration of 0·14%. The phage can then be stored for 12–18 months at 4°C.

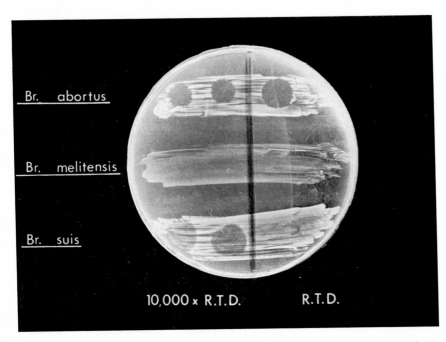

FIG. 3. The effect of Brucella phage at RTD and 10,000 × RTD on the three species of *Brucella*.

Routine Test Dilution (RTD). The RTD is assayed by making serial tenfold dilutions of phage in peptone water. A plate of serum dextrose agar is flooded with an overnight suspension of the propagating strain and allowed to dry for 1 to 2 h at 37°C. One drop (approx. 0·02 ml) of each phage dilution is placed on the inoculated plates, incubated for 48 h and then read. The RTD is the highest dilution that causes complete lysis of the culture. The RTD and 10,000 × RTD are also checked, using all three phages and FAO/WHO reference strains of *Brucella*, viz. *B. melitensis* 16M, *B. abortus* 544 and *B. suis* 1330. Figure 3 shows a typical result obtained with Tbilisi phage.

6. *Oxidative metabolism tests*

The oxidative metabolism of the cultures is determined using a Warburg apparatus. Resting cell suspensions are prepared by washing off the 48-h growth on serum dextrose agar in N saline. The cells are centrifuged and resuspended in Sörensen's phosphate buffer, pH 7·0, and adjusted to an opacity standard (which represents 0·8 mg/Nitrogen/ml).

The following substrates are used:

Group 1: L-alanine; L-asparagine; L-glutamic acid
Group 2: L-arginine; DL-ornithine; DL-citrulline; L-lysine
Group 3: L-arabinose; D-galactose; D-ribose; D-xylose.

They are made as 1% (w/v) solutions in Sörensen's phosphate buffer, pH 7·0. (The pH of the glutamic acid has to be adjusted by the addition of KOH.)

In addition, strips of Whatman No. 1 filter paper and 20% (w/v) KOH solution are required.

The flask constant K (Vol. of gas × 0·088—volume of substrate × 0·085) is worked out for each manometer and flask.

Flask No. 1 (Control for endogenous respiration) contains 1·9 ml buffer and 1·0 ml bacterial cells; flasks 2–12 contain 0·5 ml of the appropriate substrate (in side arm), 1·4 ml of buffer and 1·0 ml bacterial cells; flask 13 (Control for temperature and pressure fluctuations), contains 3·0 ml buffer.

0·1 ml of 20% KOH is placed into the centre well of flasks 1–12, together with a piece of filter paper.

The manometers and flasks are assembled, and the substrate is then tipped from the side arm into the flask and the flasks placed in the water bath at 37°C with the manometer taps open, and shaking started. After 20 min, the manometer fluid is raised to the 150 mark, and the taps closed.

After 20 min, the system is stopped, the manometer fluid adjusted so that the right arm is at the 150 mark; if the left arm is at 75 or less, the reading is noted, the manometer tap opened and the fluid again adjusted to 150, and the tap closed. If the manometer reading is over 75, it is left. Three such readings are made every 20 min and after 1 h the final manometer readings are taken, the taps opened and the flasks placed in a saturated solution of KOH in alcohol. The final QO₂N values are calculated as follows:

Time (min)	Manometer 1	Manometer 2	
0	150	150	
20	130	60 (reset)	150—60 = 90
40	100	70 (reset)	150—70 = 80
60 min	70	80	150—80 = 70
	150—70 = 80		240

Correct each figure for the temperature control, if necessary.

TABLE 6. Comparison of expected* oxidative rates (QO$_2$N) which characterize type 1 of each species of *Brucella* with observed rates of type 2 and type 3 variants (data from Meyer and Cameron, 1961b)

Species and types of *Brucella*	Group 1 substrates				Group 2 substrates				Group 3 substrates			
	L-alanine	L-aspara-gine	L-glutamic acid	L-aspartic acid	L-arginine	DL-citrul-line	L-lysine	DL-ornithine	L-arabinose	D-galactose	D-ribose	D-xylose
B. melitensis expected rate range	38-214	51-199	48-420	0-173	0-31	0-34	0-39	0-48	0-41	0-40	0-54	0-62
B. abortus type 1 expected rate range	53-149	69-189	74-414	0-98	7-45	0-48	0-37	9-53	30-164	95-291	148-384	29-43
type 2 observed range	68-113	90-150	130-178	10-52	16-32	8-31	4-21	0-40	68-108	126-210	192-315	20-80
type 3 observed range	89-113	98-117	208-283	14-22	35-61	15-25	7-40	8-25	46-111	101-160	226-307	17-33
B. suis type 1 expected rate range	5-73	0-30	0-71	0-28	34-126	48-200	50-166	60-264	116-524	0-475	219-501	72-306
type 2 observed range	0-190	0-119	50-177	0-67	45-111	86-187	0-34	93-278	107-412	37-172	200-433	68-180
type 3 observed range	10-106	0-22	40-379	0-33	45-108	65-123	46-145	104-216	20-54	8-237	204-401	28-83

* Mean of observed rate $\pm 2\sigma$.

Manometer 1   80 × Flask Constant ÷ 0·8 = endogenous rate X
Manometer 2 240 × Flask Constant ÷ 0·8 = Y
∴ QO₂N for substrate = Y − X = Z

Values are similarly worked out for each substrate.

The preceding table (Table 6) taken from Meyer and Cameron (1961b) gives the expected oxidative rates of the type I of each *Brucella* species and the observed rate for the type II and III variants.

Procedure

In the identification of a brucella culture it is essential to include in all the tests the three reference strains, viz. *B. melitensis* 16M, *B. abortus* 544 and *B. suis* 1330 as a check on media and methods.

1. The culture is streaked on glycerin-dextrose agar and incubated for 4 days in an atmosphere containing 10% (v/v) added CO_2; the plate is then examined under obliquely transmitted light.

2. A typical smooth colony is picked and streaked on three slopes of serum-dextrose agar. One slope is incubated in the ordinary atmosphere and the other two with 10% added CO_2. A strip of lead-acetate paper is inserted in one of the slopes incubated in the CO_2 enriched atmosphere.

3. The lead-acetate strips are examined each day; if any blackening occurs, the strip is changed.

4. After 4 days the slope incubated in air is examined to see if growth has occurred.

5. After 2 to 3 days of incubation, one of the two slopes incubated in the CO_2 atmosphere is examined, as follows:

   (i) Slide agglutination tests are made with monospecific abortus and melitensis antisera diluted 1/5 in phenol saline. A drop of each serum is placed on a clean slide and the growth emulsified. The suspension must not be too thick, as otherwise agglutination is delayed. The slide is gently rocked and examined with the naked eye. Agglutination in the form of macroscopic clumping occurs within a minute or so.

   (ii) The growth from the slope is emulsified in buffered saline (pH 6·8) to give a suspension containing approximately 10^{10} cells/ml, and used to inoculate dye plates which have been incubated overnight. Each plate is divided into four and a loopful of the suspension is streaked five times on the quarter plate without recharging the loop (Fig. 4). The loop is sterilized between each plate. After drying, the plates are incubated for 4 days in the CO_2-enriched atmosphere and examined after 5 days. The results are recorded as either negative or as 1+ to 5+, depending whether growth has occurred on one or all five strokes.

(iii) A loopful of the suspension is streaked across a well-dried serum-dextrose agar plate and allowed to dry for 1 h at 37°C. It is usually possible to inoculate up to six cultures per plate. Drops of phage at RTD and at 10,000 × RTD are placed on the culture, allowed to dry and examined after 24–48 h of incubation (see Fig. 3).

A   **B**

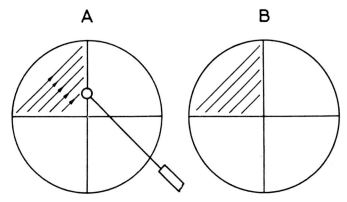

FIG. 4. Use of loop for inoculating dye-plates with Brucella strains. A = basic fuchsin; B = thionin.

(iv) Roux flasks containing serum-dextrose agar are inoculated with the suspension and incubated for 48–72 h. The growth is harvested, washed, standardized and used as resting cell suspensions for oxidative metabolism tests (already detailed).

The authors wish to thank the World Health Organization for permission to reproduce Figs. 1 and 4, and also Mr R. Sayer for care in taking the photographs.

References

BIBERSTEIN, E. L., & CAMERON, H. S. (1961). The family Brucellaceae in veterinary research. *A. Rev. Microbiol.*, **15**, 93.

BUDDLE, M. B. (1956). Studies on *Brucella ovis* (n.sp.), a cause of genital disease of sheep in New Zealand and Australia. *J. Hyg., Camb.*, **54**, 351.

CRUICKSHANK, J. C. (1957). The duration of bacteraemia in relation to the virulence of Brucella strains. *J. Hyg., Camb.*, **55**, 140.

DAVYDOV, N. N. (1961). Properties of brucella isolated from reindeer. *Trudy vsesoyuz. Inst. eksp. Vet.*, **27**, 24 (*Vet. Bull., Weybridge* (1962), **32**, 2189).

HENRY, B. S. (1933). Dissociation in the genus Brucella. *J. infect. Dis.*, **52**, 374.

HUDDLESON, I. F. (1929). The differentiation of the species of the genus Brucella. *Mich. State College agric. Exp. Sta., Techn. Bull.* No. 100.

HUDDLESON, I. F. (1943). *Brucellosis in man and animals.* Rev. ed. New York: Commonwealth Fund.

HUDDLESON, I. F. (1961). Emergence during growth of Brucella strains on dye-agar media of cells that show changes in sulfur metabolism. *Bull. Wld Hlth Org.*, **24**, 91.

JONES, L. M. (1958). A recommended method for the preparation of monospecific brucella sera. *Bull. Wld Hlth Org.*, **19**, 177.

MEYER, M. E. (1961). Metabolic characterization of the genus Brucella. IV. Correlation of oxidative metabolic patterns and susceptibility to Brucella bacteriophage type abortus, strain 3. *J. Bact.*, **82**, 950.

MEYER, M. E., & CAMERON, H. S. (1961a). Metabolic characterization of the genus Brucella. *J. Bact.*, **82**, 387.

MEYER, M. E., & CAMERON, H. S. (1961b). Metabolic characterization of the genus Brucella. II. Oxidative metabolic patterns of the described biotypes. *J. Bact.*, **82**, 396.

MEYER, M. E., & MORGAN, W. J. BRINLEY (1962). Metabolic characterization of Brucella strains that show conflicting identity by biochemical and serological methods. *Bull. Wld Hlth Org.*, **26**, 823.

MORGAN, W. J. BRINLEY (1961). The use of the thionin blue sensitivity test in the examination of brucella. *J. gen. Microbiol.*, **25**, 135.

MORGAN, W. J. BRINLEY (1963). The examination of brucella cultures for lysis by phage. *J. gen. Microbiol.*, **30**, 437.

MORGAN, W. J. BRINLEY (1964). Reviews of the progress of dairy science. Section E. Diseases of dairy cattle. Brucellosis. *J. Dairy Res.*, **31**, 315.

RENOUX, G. (1958). The concept of species in the genus Brucella. *Annls. Inst. Pasteur, Paris*, **94**, 179.

STABLEFORTH, A. W. (1959). Species of Brucella and their general distribution, p. 83. In STABLEFORTH, A. W., & GALLOWAY, I. A. *Infectious diseases of domestic animals. Diseases due to bacteria*, Vol. 1. London: Butterworths.

STABLEFORTH, A. W., & JONES, L. M. (1963). Report of the subcommittee on the taxonomy of the genus Brucella. Speciation in the genus Brucella. *Int. Bull. bact. Nomencl. Taxon.*, **13**, 145.

STOENNER, H. G., & LACKMAN, D. B. (1957). A new species of Brucella isolated from the desert wood rat, *Neotoma lepida*, Thomas. *Am. J. vet. Res.*, **18**, 947.

WHITE, P. G., & WILSON, J. B. (1951). Differentiation of smooth and non-smooth colonies of Brucellae. *J. Bact.*, **61**, 239.

WILSON, G. S., & MILES, A. A. (1932). The serological differentiation of smooth strains of the Brucella group. *Br. J. exp. Path.*, **13**, 1.

Methods for the Characterization of the Bacteroidaceae

ELLA M. BARNES AND C. S. IMPEY

Low Temperature Research Station, Cambridge, England

AND

H. S. GOLDBERG

*Department of Microbiology, School of Medicine,
University of Missouri, U.S.A.*

The anaerobic, non-sporing, Gram-negative bacteria occur in large numbers in the alimentary tract of man and other animals and are frequently associated with necrotic lesions. Owing to difficulties in isolation, however, comparatively little is known about them and there is no generally accepted scheme for their classification. It is only possible at present to describe tests for their separation into well-defined groups which may or may not relate to the genera described by Breed *et al.* (1957). Recent studies on these organisms have been carried out by Baird-Parker (1960), Fievez (1963) and Beerens *et al.* (1963).

Four organisms may be considered representative of some of the major groups within the Family Bacteroidaceae: *Fusobacterium polymorphum, Fusobacterium biacutum, Sphaerophorus necrophorus* and *Bacteroides convexus* (Syn. *Ristella convexa* or *Eggerthella convexa*). Their differential characteristics are given below. A fifth group of organisms, not included here, is represented by *Bacteroides melaninogenicus*, which requires haemin and menadione for growth.

Media

Reinforced Clostridial Agar or Broth (RCM) of Hirsch and Grinsted (1954). Peptone (Evans) 10 g; beef extract (Lab-Lemco, Oxoid) 10 g; yeast extract (Oxoid) 3 g; cysteine hydrochloride 0·5 g; glucose 5 g; sodium acetate anhyd. 5 g; soluble starch 1 g; agar (New Zealand) 0·5 g; distilled water 1 l, pH 7·2–7·4. For the solid medium use agar (New Zealand) 12 g/l.

VL medium (Beerens, personal communication). Tryptone (Oxoid) 10 g; NaCl 5 g; beef extract (Lab-Lemco, Oxoid) 3 g; yeast extract (Difco) 5 g; cysteine hydrochloride 0·4 g; glucose, 2 g; agar (New Zealand) 0·6 g;

IMM–C

distilled water 1 l, pH 7·2–7·4. For the solid medium use agar (New Zealand) 12 g/l.

Basal Medium (Beerens, 1954). Peptone (Evans) 10 g; NaCl 5 g; beef extract (Lab-Lemco, Oxoid) 3 g; yeast extract (Oxoid), 5 g; cysteine hydrochloride 0·4 g; agar (New Zealand) 0·6 g; distilled water 1 l, pH 7·2–7·4.

BGP. Basal medium + 0·1% glucose + 0·4% Na_2HPO_4.

BGP (maintenance). BGP with 1·5% of gelatin added.

All of the liquid media are sterilized at a pressure of 15 lb/in² for 15 min in 19-ml lots in screw-capped 1-oz bottles.

Before inoculation they are held in a boiling-water bath for 20 min, cooled and used immediately.

In every case (except for H_2S production, the detection of volatile fatty acids, or when RCM or VL broth is used) a 3% solution of sodium formaldehyde sulphoxalate, sterilized by filtration, is added to the medium immediately before use to give a final concentration of 0·03% (Riemann, 1957).

Agar plates

For growth on agar plates a reducing medium such as RCM or VL should be used. This may be supplemented with 5% horse blood. All plates are poured on the day of use. Immediately after inoculation (i.e. within 10 min) they should be placed in anaerobic jars in an atmosphere of hydrogen (90%) and carbon dioxide (10%). Incubate at 37°C for about 3 days.

Growth tests, morphology, etc.

Use either RCM or VL broth. Inoculate with 0·25 ml of a 24–48 h culture and incubate at 37° for 1–5 days. Examine by phase-contrast microscopy. These organisms are often difficult to stain.

Biochemical tests

Additions are made to the "basal medium" for the various biochemical tests. Inoculate with 0·25 ml of a 24–48 h RCM or VL broth culture. All tests are incubated for 5 days at 37°C.

Carbohydrate fermentation. All carbohydrates are sterilized by filtration and added to the basal medium to give a concentration of 0·25%. Change in pH is determined by the capillator technique (B.D.H. Ltd.).

Hydrogen sulphide. To either the basal medium or BGP, 0·02% ferrous sulphate and 0·03% sodium thiosulphate is added to detect hydrogen sulphide production.

Indole. Cultures are grown in the basal medium or, where growth is poor, in BGP. Add 1 ml of ether to the culture and shake vigorously to extract the indole. Add 0·5 ml Ehrlich's reagent to the ether layer, followed by a saturated solution of potassium persulphate.

Gelatin liquefaction. BGP + 15% gelatin is used.

Skim-milk medium. Skim milk containing cysteine hydrochloride 0·08% (pH 7·4) is used to detect acid (by use of litmus paper), digestion and clot.

Detection of volatile fatty acids. The volatile fatty acids produced from glucose fermentation are determined by the method of Guillaume *et al.* (1956), as modified by Charles and Barrett (1963).

Bile stimulation. Bile 10% is added to BGP medium (Beerens and Castel, 1960).

Inhibition by brilliant green. Brilliant green (93% active dye) is added to BGP or RCM to give a concentration of 1:100,000.

Threonine test. The method of Beerens *et al.* (1959) is used to detect threonine utilization. This test has recently been simplified by Beerens (personal communication).

Antibiotic sensitivities. Antibiotic solutions are added to one of the growth media to give the required concentrations.

Maintenance of stock cultures

Organisms grown in the unbuffered RCM or VL medium may die in less than a week, so for stock cultures it is better to use BGP (maintenance) and store at 1°–5°C. Even so many of these organisms are not viable for longer than 3–4 weeks and should therefore be freeze-dried as soon as possible after isolation (Barnes and Goldberg, 1962).

Morphological and physiological properties of representative strains

Hitherto, traditional tests including morphology, indole production, hydrogen sulphide production and the fermentation of various carbohydrates have been used to identify the Gram-negative anaerobes. Several of these tests, such as carbohydrate fermentation, are variable even for the same strain, and new tests have been developed, in particular by Dr H. Beerens (Institut Pasteur, Lille). The following tests have proved useful for differentiating the various species and genera. 1. The terminal pH in glucose broth and the types of volatile fatty acids produced, i.e. formic, acetic, propionic or butyric acids. 2. The production of propionic acid from threonine. 3. Growth stimulation by bile. 4. The effect of various inhibitors, in particular polymyxin (10µg/ml) and brilliant green 1:100,000.

The properties of four typical strains are shown in Figs. 1–4 and Tables 1 and 2. *Fusobacterium polymorphum,* and *Fusobacterium biacutum* have the characteristic cells with pointed ends as shown in Figs. 1 and 2, whilst *Bacteroides convexus* has cells with rounded ends (Fig. 4). The strain of *Sphaerophorus necrophorus* shown in Fig. 3 is not pleomorphic, but other strains of *Sphaerophorus* frequently show long filaments and short rods in the same culture.

The characters given in Table 1 demonstrate the difficulties of using the more traditional tests for separating these organisms. On the other hand,

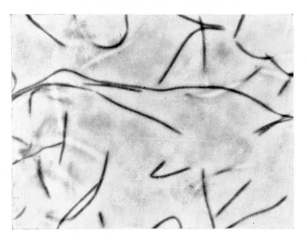

Fig. 1

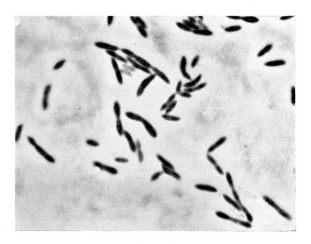

Fig. 2

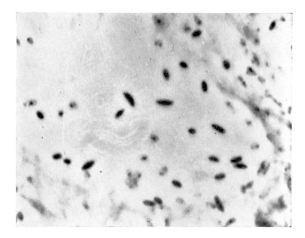

FIG. 3

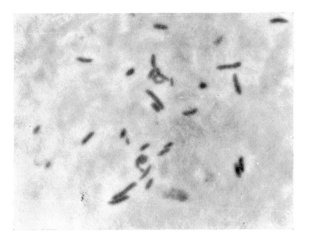

FIG. 4

FIGS. 1–4. Appearance under phase contrast of strains grown in VL broth for 24 h at 37° (× 1500). (1) *Fusobacterium polymorphum*. (2) *Fusobacterium biacutum*. (3) *Sphaerophorus necrophorus*. (4) *Bacteroides convexus*.

considerable success has been obtained from using some of the tests shown in Table 2. These tests were mainly developed for the human isolates, but it is the experience of the authors that they have also helped in differentiating previously unidentified strains from animal sources (Goldberg *et al.*, 1964).

TABLE 1. Some properties of representative strains

	Acid from									Behaviour in cysteine milk	Production of		
	Sucrose	Cellobiose	Arabinose	Galactose	Glycerol	Inositol	Mannitol	Salicin	Xylose		Indole	Hydrogen sulphide	Gelatin liquefaction
Fusobacterium polymorphum (ATCC 10953)	+ (V)	−	−	+	−	−	−	−	−	No change	+	+++‡	−
Fusobacterium biacutum＊	−	−	+	+	−	−	+	−	−	Acid and clot	−	+++	−
Sphaerophorus necrophorus＊	−	− (V)	−	+ (V)	−	−	−	−	−	No change	+ (V)	+++	−
Bacteroides convexus＊ syn. *Eggerthella convexa*	+	−	− (V)	+	−	−	−	− (V)	+ (V)	Acid	− (V)	+	−

+ positive test.
− negative test.
(V) variable result for different strains.
＊ Strains kindly supplied by Dr H. Beerens, Institut Pasteur, Lille.
‡ Hydrogen sulphide production, +++ strongly positive, + weak reaction.

TABLE 2. Differential properties of representative strains

| | Propionic acid from threonine | Copious gas production † | Glucose fermentation | | | | | | | Growth stimulated by 10% bile | Growth in presence of | |
| | | | Terminal pH | | Volatile fatty acids produced | | | | Acid from mannitol | | Polymyxin 10μg/ml. | brilliant green 1/100,000 |
			4·6–5·5	5·6–6·2	Formic	Acetic	Propionic	Butyric				
Fusobacterium polymorphum (ATCC 10953)	+	−	−	+	+	+	−	+	−	−	−	+
*Fusobacterium biacutum**	+	+	−	+	+	+	−	+	+	−	−	−
*Sphaerophorus necrophorus**	+	+ (V)	−	+	+	+	+	+	−	−	−	+
*Bacteroides convexus** syn. *Eggerthella convexa*	−	−	+	−	− (V)	+	+‡	−	+	+	+	−

+ positive test.
− negative test.
(V) variable result for different strains.
* Strains kindly supplied by Dr H. Beerens, Institut Pasteur, Lille.
† RCM or VL broth.
‡ Some strains produce only a trace of propionic acid.

References

BAIRD-PARKER, A. C. (1960). The classification of fusobacteria from the human mouth. *J. gen. Microbiol.*, **22**, 458.

BARNES, E. M., & GOLDBERG, H. S. (1962). The isolation of anaerobic Gram-negative bacteria from poultry reared with and without antibiotic supplements. *J. appl. Bact.*, **25**, 94.

BEERENS, H. (1954). Amélioration des techniques d'étude et d'identification des bacteriés anaérobies. *Ann. Inst. Pasteur, Lille*, **6**, 36.

BEERENS, H., & CASTEL, M. M. (1960). Action de la bile sur la croissance de certaines bactéries anaérobies à Gram-négatif. *Ann. Inst. Pasteur.*, **99**, 454.

BEERENS, H., GUILLAUME, J., & PETIT, H. (1959). Étude de la fermentation propionique de la L(—) thréonine par 45 souches de bactéries anaérobies non sporulées à Gram négatif. *Ann. Inst. Pasteur*, **96**, 211.

BEERENS, H., SCHAFFNER, Y., GUILLAUME, J., & CASTEL, M. M. (1963). Les bacilles anaérobies non sporulés à Gram négatif favorisés par la bile. Leur appartenance au genre Eggerthella (nov. gen). *Ann. Inst. Pasteur, Lille*, **14**, 5.

BREED, R. S., MURRAY, E. G. D., & SMITH, N. R. (1957). *Bergey's Manual of Determinative Bacteriology*, 7th ed. London: Ballière, Tindall & Cox.

CHARLES, A. B., & BARRETT, F. C. (1963). Detection of volatile fatty acids produced by obligate Gram-negative anaerobes. *J. Med. Lab. Technol.*, **20**, 266.

FIEVEZ, L. (1963). *Étude compareé des souches de* Sphaerophorus necrophorus *isolées chez l'homme et chez l'animal*. Brussels: Presses Académiques Européennes.

GOLDBERG, H. S., BARNES, E. M., & CHARLES, A. B. (1964). Unusual Bacteroides-like organism. *J. Bact.*, **87**, 737.

GUILLAUME, J., BEERENS, H., & OSTEUX, R. (1956). La chromatographie sur papier des acides aliphatiques volatils de C_1 a C_6. Son application à la détermination des bactéries anaérobies. *Ann. Inst. Pasteur Lille*, **8**, 13.

HIRSCH, A., & GRINSTED, E. (1954). Methods for the growth and enumeration of anaerobic spore formers from cheese with observations on the effect of nisin. *J. Dairy Res.*, **21**, 101.

RIEMANN, H. (1957). Some observations on the germination of *Clostridium* spores and the subsequent delay before the commencement of vegetative growth. *J. appl. Bact.*, **20**, 404.

Methods for Classifying Staphylococci and Micrococci

A. C. BAIRD-PARKER

*Unilever Research Laboratory, Colworth House,
Sharnbrook, Bedford, England*

Classification of the Gram-positive and catalase-positive cocci belonging to the aerobic genera of the Micrococcaceae is still controversial. Some progress towards a stable and rational classification of these organisms has been made by the International Subcommittee on Staphylococci and Micrococci (1965), which has recently proposed a standard test for separating these organisms into two genera, the genus *Staphylococcus* and the genus *Micrococcus*: the genus *Staphylococcus* should contain the mainly parasitic, facultative-anaerobic cocci producing acid from glucose under anaerobic conditions, and the genus *Micrococcus* should contain the mainly saprophytic, aerobic cocci that will produce acid from glucose aerobically but not anaerobically. This division is supported by a number of other characters and details of these will be found in my previous publications (Baird-Parker, 1962, 1963, 1965*a*, *b*).

It is currently thought that the aerobic packet-formers previously classified in the genus *Sarcina* are insufficiently distinct from micrococci to warrant separate generic rank, and it has been suggested, therefore, that the genus *Sarcina* should only contain the anaerobic packet-formers (Shaw *et al.*, 1951; Kocur and Martinec, 1962).

Separation of Members of the Genus *Staphylococcus* from Members of the Genus *Micrococcus*

The following method and medium is based on that proposed by the International Sub-committee on Staphylococci and Micrococci (1965). It gives identical results to the modified Hugh and Leifson method suggested by Baird-Parker (1963), but has the advantage that anaerobic acid production is more rapid in the proposed richer medium.

Inoculum

Check that the organism is a Gram-positive coccus and produces catalase on media with 1% glucose; failure to do this may result in the classification of a completely unrelated organism. Grow for 24 h at 37° on a tryptone, yeast-extract medium containing (% w/v): Difco tryptone 1·0; Difco yeast extract 0·1 and agar 1·5.

Preparation and use of medium

The following ingredients are dissolved in distilled water (% w/v): Difco tryptone 1·0; Difco yeast extract 0·1; glucose 1·0; bromocresol purple 0·004; Difco agar 0·2; pH 7·2. Dispense in 10-ml amounts into 6 × ½ in test tubes and sterilize by autoclaving for 20 min at 115°C. If stored, the medium should be steamed before use and rapidly cooled by standing in a bath of iced water. Duplicate tubes are heavily inoculated throughout their length with a long wire loop, and one tube of each pair is then covered with a 1–2 in layer of sterile liquid paraffin. Tubes are incubated at 37° for 5 days.

Interpretation of results

If acid is produced *throughout* both tubes the organism is a *Staphylococcus*. No acid or acid only in the aerobic tube (together with sometimes acid at the surface of the medium in the sealed tube) is diagnosed as a *Micrococcus*. Examples are shown in Fig. 1.

Separation of Organisms
within the Genera *Staphylococcus* and *Micrococcus*

A number of schemes have been proposed for dividing the genera *Staphylococcus* and *Micrococcus* into species, "groups" or "subgroups". Details of these will be found in papers by Hucker (1924, 1928), Abd-El-Malek and Gibson (1948), Shaw *et al.* (1951), Hill (1959), Anderson (1962), Kocur and Martinec (1962), Pike (1962), Mossel (1962) and Baird-Parker (1963, 1965a). At present, none of these classifications is acceptable to all taxonomists. It is, however, agreed that there are at least two species of staphylococci, namely *S. aureus* and *S. epidermidis*, and two well-defined species of micrococci, namely *M. luteus* and *M. roseus*. Undoubtedly other species will be recognized eventually and these will be given specific names when they have been adequately defined. Therefore, in order not to prejudice future binomial classifications of staphylococci and micrococci I have classified micrococci and staphylococci into "subgroups". The advantage of this type of classification is that it is flexible and subgroups can be created or combined without regard to the rigid rules attached to binomial classifications.

The main characters distinguishing the subgroups are displayed in

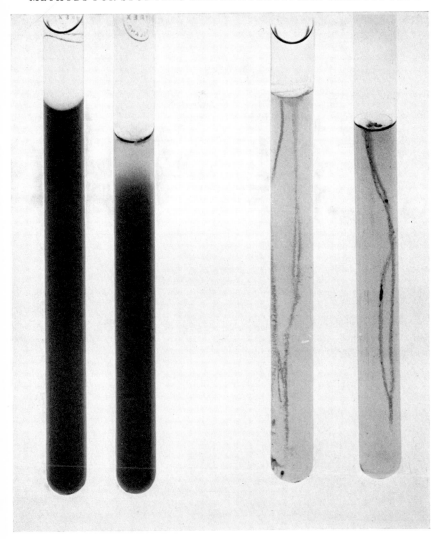

FIG. 1. Typical appearance of a staphylococcus and a micrococcus in the double-tube oxidation/fermentation test. Left to right:

Anaerobic tube with no oxidation or fermentation (*Micrococcus*); aerobic tube with oxidative attack on sugar (*Micrococcus*); anaerobic tube showing fermentation (*Staphylococcus*); aerobic tube showing oxidative growth and fermentation (*Staphylococcus*).

The dark appearance of the tubes inoculated with the *Micrococcus* is caused by the purple indicator which becomes yellow when acid is formed.

TABLE 1. Diagnostic scheme for classifying staphylococci and micrococci

	Group I *Staphylococcus* Rosenbach						Group II *Micrococcus* Cohn							
Subgroup:	I	II	III	IV	V	VI	1	2	3	4	5	6	7	8
Pink pigment	−	−	−	−	−	−	−	−	−	−	−	−	−	+
Acid from glucose:														
(1) aerobic	+	+	+	+	+	+	+	+	+	+	+	+	±	±
(2) anaerobic	+	+	+	+	+	+	−	−	−	−	−	−	−	−
Coagulase	+	−	−	−	−	−	−	−	−	−	−	−	−	−
Phosphatase	+	+	+	−	−	−	−	−	−	−	−	+	−	−
Acetoin	+	+	−	+	+	+	+	+	+	+	−	−	−	−
Acid from:														
(1) arabinose	−	−	−	−	−	−	−	−	−	+	v	+	−	−
(2) lactose	+	+	v	−	+	v	−	+	v	+	+	+	−	−
(3) maltose	+	+	−	v	+	v	v	+	+	+	+	+	−	±
(4) mannitol	+	−	−	−	−	+	−	−	+	+	+	+	−	−

± = weak or negative. v = variable.

Table 1. Staphylococcus subgroup I corresponds to *S. aureus* and subgroups II–VI to *S. epidermidis*; *Micrococcus* subgroup 7 corresponds to *M. luteus* and subgroup 8 to *M. roseus*. Further information concerning the characters of these subgroups and their relation to each other and to further species of staphylococci and micrococci can be found in previous publications (Baird-Parker, 1963, 1965a).

Determination of characters of subgroups

It is suggested that the following procedure should be used to characterize an isolate. Growth from tryptone + yeast-extract agar is used to inoculate Difco heart-infusion broth and the modified Hugh and Leifson test for separating staphylococci from micrococci. After incubation at 30° for 24 h, growth from the heart-infusion broth is used to inoculate media for phosphatase determination and for acetoin production. At the same time, other media are inoculated to determine acid production from sugars and coagulase activity.

Acid production from sugars. Medium (% w/v): $NH_4H_2PO_4$ 0·1; KCl 0·02; $MgSO_4$, $7H_2O$ 0·02; Bromocresol purple 0·004; agar 1·5; pH 7·0. The medium is dispensed in 95-ml amounts and sterilized by autoclaving at 121° for 15 min. For use, 5 ml of a 10% (w/v) Seitz-filtered solution of arabinose, lactose, maltose, or mannitol is added to a bottle of the molten base and plates poured. After drying, plates are inoculated from the heart-infusion broth and incubated at 30°. Not more than four isolates should be inoculated, each as a single streak, on to each plate and plates should be examined for acid production *daily* for 7 days.

Acetoin production. Medium (% w/v): Tryptone 1·0; Lab-Lemco 0·3; yeast extract 0·1; glucose 2·0; pH 7·2. The medium is dispensed in 5-ml amounts into 1-oz screw-capped McCartney bottles and sterilized by autoclaving at 115° for 20 min. Inoculated bottles are incubated for 14 days at 30° and the presence of acetoin tested by Barritt's modification of the VP test (Barritt, 1936). It is necessary to shake the bottles vigorously for at least 30 sec after adding the reagents, otherwise weak acetoin producers may not be detected. Tubes are read after 1 and 2 h at room temperature; a definite reddening of the culture supernatant indicates the presence of acetoin.

Phosphatase production. Medium (% w/v): Evans peptone 0·5; Lab-Lemco 0·5; NaCl 0·5; agar 1·5; pH 7·2. To 100 ml of molten base is added 1 ml of a 1% (w/v) Seitz-filtered solution of phenolphthalein diphosphate (pentasodium salt; Barber and Kuper, 1951). Incubate for 3 days at 30°.

Phosphatase activity is detected by inverting the agar plate over a Petridish lid containing 0·880 sp. gr. ammonia; colonies of phosphatase-producing organisms turn a deep-pink on exposure to the ammonia vapours.

Coagulase production. 0·1 ml of the overnight heart-infusion broth culture is pipetted into a $3 \times \frac{3}{8}$ in tube. Difco rabbit plasma (0·3 ml) is added and, after mixing, incubated at 37°. The tube is examined for coagulation of the plasma after incubation for 1, 2, 4, 8 and 24 h. Any degree of coagulation of the plasma is evidence of coagulase activity.

Pigmentation. Pink pigment characteristic of *Micrococcus roseus* (*Micrococcus* subgroup 8) will be apparent on the phenolphthalein disposphate plates after incubation at 30° for 3 days.

References

ABD-EL-MALEK, Y., & GIBSON, T. (1948). Studies in the bacteriology of milk. II. The staphylococci and micrococci of milk. *J. Dairy Res.*, **15**, 249.

ANDERSON, J. I. W. (1962). Studies on micrococci isolated from the North Sea. *J. appl. Bact.*, **25**, 362.

BAIRD-PARKER, A. C. (1962). The occurrence and enumeration, according to a new classification, of micrococci and staphylococci in bacon and on human and pig skin. *J. appl. Bact.*, **25**, 352.

BAIRD-PARKER, A. C. (1963). A classification of micrococci and staphylococci based on physiological and biochemical tests. *J. gen. Microbiol.*, **30**, 409.

BAIRD-PARKER, A. C. (1965a). The classification of staphylococci and micrococci from world-wide sources. *J. gen. Microbiol.*, **38**, 363.

BAIRD-PARKER, A. C. (1965b). Staphylococci and their classification. *Ann. N.Y. Acad. Sci.*, **128**, 4.

BARBER, M., & KUPER, S. W. A. (1951). Identification of *Staphylococcus pyogenes* by the phosphatase reaction. *J. Path. Bact.*, **63**, 65.

BARRITT, M. M. (1936). The intensification of the Voges-Proskauer reaction by the addition of α-naphthol. *J. Path. Bact.*, **42**, 441.

KOCUR, M., & MARTINEC, T. (1962). *A Taxonomic Study of the Genus Micrococcus.* Brno (Czechoslovakia): Fac. Sci. Univ. Purkyně.

HILL, L. R. (1959). The Adansonian classification of the staphylococci. *J. gen. Microbiol.*, **20**, 277.

HUCKER, C. J. (1924). Studies on the Coccaceae. II. A study of the general characters of the micrococci. *Tech. Bull. N.Y. St. agric. Exp. Sta. No. 100.*

HUCKER, C. J. (1928). Studies on the Coccaceae. IX. Further studies on the classification of the micrococci. *Tech. Bull. N.Y. St. agric. Exp. Sta. No. 135.*

INTERNATIONAL SUBCOMMITTEE ON STAPHYLOCOCCI AND MICROCOCCI (1965). Recommendations of subcommittee. *Int. Bull. bact. Nomencl. Taxon.* **15**, 109.

MOSSELL, D. A. A. (1962). Attempt in classification of catalase-positive staphylococci and micrococci. *J. Bact.*, **84**, 1140.

PIKE, E. B. (1962). The classification of staphylococci and micrococci from the human mouth. *J. appl. Bact.*, **25**, 448.

SHAW, C., STITT, J. M., & COWAN, S. T. (1951). Staphylococci and their classification. *J. gen. Microbiol.*, **5**, 1010.

Identification of the Lactic Acid Bacteria

M. Elisabeth Sharpe and T. F. Fryer

*National Institute for Research in Dairying,
Shinfield, Reading, Berkshire, England*

AND

D. G. Smith*

Queen Elizabeth College, London, England

The genera dealt with here include those members of the family *Lactobacillaceae* (Breed *et al.*, 1957) most commonly encountered in food and dairy products, in the mouth and intestinal tract of humans and animals, and in vegetable material; a few pathogenic species are also included. *Diplococcus* and *Peptostreptococcus* among the *Streptococceae*, and the strictly anaerobic intestinal genera among the *Lactobacilleae* are not included.

Lactic acid bacteria are Gram-positive, non-sporulating cocci or rods dividing in one plane only, with the exception of the pediococci; catalase negative (some strains may possess a "pseudocatalase" detectable on low sugar containing media; see section on *Pediococcus*), usually non-motile, obligate fermenters, producing mainly lactic acid and sometimes also volatile acids and CO_2.

They are subdivided into genera as follows:

Streptococcus. Homofermentative cocci in pairs or chains.
Leuconostoc. Heterofermentative cocci in pairs or chains.
Pediococcus. Homofermentative cocci dividing in two planes to give tetrads which may appear as clusters (Gunther, 1959).
Lactobacillus. Homofermentative or heterofermentative rods.

Characteristics Used to Define Genera of Lactic Acid Bacteria

1. Microscopic appearance, using Gram strain. Broth or semisolid media should be used to culture organisms.
2. Catalase test. Cultures grown either on a suitable nutrient agar or in broth can be used.

* *Present address:* Department of Botany, University College, London.

TABLE 1. Physiological and biochemical t⌐

Serological group	Physiological group	Sherman criteria							β haemolysis	Na hippurate hydrolysis	Lactose	Trehalose	Sorbitol	Gelatin liquefaction
		Haemolysis	Growth at 10°	Growth at 45°	Growth at pH 9·6	0·1% Methylene blue	Survive 60°/30 min.	NH_3 from arginine						
D										−	+		+	−
D									+		+		+	±
D	α, β or δ	+	+	+	+	+	+	+		−	+		+	+
D	Enterococcus									−	+		−	−
D									±		+		−	−
D	α or δ	−	+	−	−	−	−	−		−	+		∓	−
D										−	−		−	−
N														
N	Lactic	δ	−	−		+	±	±						
N														
Ungrouped											+	−		
Ungrouped	Viridans	α or δ	+	−	−	∓	−				±	±		
Ungrouped											±	∓		
A									+	−				
B									±	+				
C									+	−				
C									+	−	−		−	−
C									+	−	±		+	−
C	Pyogenic	β	−	−	−	−	−	+	−	−	+		+	±
C									+	−	+		−	+
E									+	−				
F									+	−				
G									+	−				
H*									±	−				

* Serological groups K–T have also been designated.   + posi⌐

3. Fermentative use of carbohydrate. The Hugh and Leifson test (1953) as described by Skerman (1959) is used. Acid is produced from glucose by fermentative organisms under both anaerobic and aerobic conditions, whilst oxidative organisms form acid only in the presence of oxygen.

4. Homofermentative or heterofermentative. Homofermentative species ferment glucose to form almost entirely lactic acid, whilst heterofermentative species produce appreciable amounts of acetic acid and CO_2 in addition. In practice they are distinguished by testing for the production of gas from glucose, using the method of Gibson and Abd-el-Malek (1945) in

urther identification of *Streptococcus* spp.

cies Differentiation

Glycerol (anaerobic)	Tetrazolium reduction	Growth at 50°	Mannitol	Arabinose	Melibiose	Melezitose	Maltose	Growth at 40°	Growth at pH 9·2	Growth in 4% NaCl	NH₃ from arginine	Acetoin production	*Streptococcus* spp.	Usual habitat or source	
+	+	−	+	−	−	+							*faecalis*		
+	+	−	+	−	−	+							*faecalis* var. *zymogenes*	Intestine of	
+	+	−	+	−	−	+							*faecalis* var. *liquefaciens*	man and other warm-blooded	
−	−	+	+	+	+	−							*faecium*	animals	
−	−	−	+	−	−	−							*durans*		Mostly non-pathogenic
−	±	−	∓	±	+	−							*bovis*	Bovine intestine	
−	−	−	−	−	−	−							*equinus*	Equine intestine	
							+	+	+	+	+	−	*lactis*	Dairy utensils, milk	
							+	+	+	+	+	+	*lactis* var. *diacetilactis*	and milk products,	
							−	−	−	−	−	−	*cremoris*	vegetable material	
		+	−				−					−	*thermophilus*	Pasteurized milk and cheese	
		−	−					+				−	*salivarius*	Human mouth and throat	
								+			Sl		*mitis*	Human mouth and throat	
													pyogenes	Human—pathogen	
													agalactiae	Cattle—pathogen	
													equi	Horse—pathogen	
Serological grouping and													*equisimilis*	Human—parasite	
typing are the preferred													*dysgalactiae*	Cattle and sheep—pathogen	
methods of differentiation													*zooepidemicus*	Animal—pathogen	
in this group													sp.	Cattle—parasite	
													anginosus	Human—pathogen	
													sp.	Human and animal—parasite	
													sanguis	Human—parasite	

− negative.   Sl slight.   ± majority positive.   ∓ majority negative.

which a well-buffered nutritive agar medium containing a high concentration of glucose is inoculated with the test organism and an agar seal poured on to the surface. Production of CO_2 may be indicated merely by gas bubbles or pockets, or by the forcing of the seal up the tube. It is essential to use a heavy inoculum of a vigorously growing culture.

Streptococcus

The criteria of Sherman (1937) are still used to divide the streptococci into four groups, enterococcus, lactic, viridans and pyogenic, Table 1, but other biochemical tests and serological grouping and typing have been used as well. It should be stressed that strains are often encountered which do not fall into any group and can only be referred to as "unclassified". Detailed information on the physiology and classification of faecal streptococci is given by Shattock (1962) and Deibel (1964).

Fermentation reactions. In the enterococcus and lactic groups carbohydrate fermentations are a useful aid in identification. For example, failure to ferment lactose differentiates *S. equinus* from the other intestinal strepto-cocci (Smith and Shattock, 1962), whilst ability of *S. faecalis* to utilize glycerol anaerobically (Gunsalus, 1947) distinguishes this organism and its varieties from the other enterococci. Inability to ferment maltose charac-teristically distinguishes *S. cremoris* from other group N streptococci. Other fermentations of useful diagnostic value are those of mannitol, arabinose, melibiose, melezitose, trehalose and sucrose.

Growth temperatures. Growth in broth at 50° has been used to distinguish *S. faecium* from the other enterococci. This feature may, however, be lost on repeated subculture. Failure to grow at 40° is a useful diagnostic feature of *S. cremoris* (see Reiter and Møller-Madson, 1963, for further details on differentiation of lactic streptococci).

Haemolysis. It is important that horse blood be used for detecting haemo-lysis, as blood of other species may give different reactions. Pour plates of 5% (v/v) horse blood in nutrient agar with well-separated colonies are examined at 24 h, 48 h and after a further 24 h at 4°C (Wilson and Miles, 1955). *S. faecalis* var. *zymogenes* is readily identified by its β haemolysis; *S. durans* is also sometimes β haemolytic.

Gelatin hydrolysis. The hydrolysis of gelatin, a characteristic of *S. faecalis* var. *liquefaciens* and occasional strains of *S. faecalis* var. *zymogenes* can be detected in several ways. Gelatin (12% w/v) stabs incubated at 22° or 37°C are examined for liquefaction and failure to resolidify respectively. Alter-natively, gelatin can be incorporated into an agar plate which is streaked and, after incubation, flooded with gelatin reagent (Skerman, 1959).

Reduction reactions. *S. faecalis* and its varieties can be distinguished readily from the other faceal streptococci by their strong reducing activity.

    i. Tellurite. *S. faecalis* and varieties grow readily on glucose yeast-extract agar containing 0·04% (w/v) potassium tellurite (Skadhauge, 1950). Black colonies are produced by reduction to tellurium. The other faecal streptococci either do not grow or only produce dusty grey colonies.

    ii. Tetrazolium. *S. faecalis* and varieties reduce colourless 2,3,4-triphenyl-tetrazolium chloride (pH 6·0) to a red formazan. The test can be conducted in liquid or on solid media (Barnes, 1956).

    iii. Litmus milk. Litmus (or methylene blue) milk is reduced more rapidly by *S. faecalis* and its varieties than by other group D streptococci. Further, *S. faecalis* var. *liquefaciens* can usually be detected by liquefaction of the clot. *S. equinus* has no action on litmus milk.

Starch hydrolysis. *S. bovis* characteristically hydrolyses starch to reducing sugars. *S. equinus* may split starch, but not to the reducing-sugar level (Dunican and Seeley, 1962). Organisms are streaked on nutrient agar + 0·3% soluble starch, and after incubation for 3 days, plates are flooded with Gram's iodine solution. A colourless zone under and around the colonies denotes starch hydrolysis.

Serological tests. Streptococci can be grouped serologically using Lancefield's (1933) precipitation technique. Hydrochloric acid extracts (Lancefield, 1933) or formamide extracts (Fuller, 1938) are tested against commercially available antisera by a precipitin ring test (Shattock, 1949) or by gel diffusion, using the slide method (Mansi, 1958).

Faecal streptococci can be identified further into serological types by the precipitin test (Sharpe and Fewins, 1960; Medrek and Barnes, 1962; Sharpe, 1964).

Pyogenic streptococci are typed both by precipitation and agglutination reactions (Cruikshank, 1960). Serological differentiation is the only reliable method of identification.

Leuconostoc

The media and methods used here are those described by Garvie (1960)

TABLE 2. Physiological characteristics of the genus *Leuconostoc*

Species	L. citrovorum or L. cremoris	L. kefir or L. lactis	L. dextranicum	L. mesenteroides		
Garvie group	I	II	IV	III	V	VI
Litmus milk	—	a or AC	—	—	—	a
Growth at 37°C.	—	+	+	+	+	+
Resistance 55° 15 min	—	+	±	±	±	±
Dextran synthesis	—	—	+ sl	—	+	+
Diacetyl produced	+	∓	—			—
Acid from:						
arabinose	—	—	—	+	—	+
xylose	—	—	—	∓	+	+
salicin	—	—	—	—	—	+
sucrose	—	+	+	+	+	+
melibiose	—	+	—	+	+	+
lactose	+	+	—	±	±	±
trehalose	—	—	+	+	+	+
Aesculin hydrolysed	—	—	—	±	±	+

a = slight acid. AC = acid, clot. sl = slight.

None hydrolyse arginine; none grow at 45°C. All produce gas from glucose; all form D(−) lactic acid.

and the scheme of identification (Table 2) is based on those of Abd-el-Malek and Gibson (1948) and of Garvie (1960).

Production of diacetyl. Absence of diacetyl production distinguishes *Leuc. dextranicum* and *Leuc. mesenteroides* from the other species, the method of Eggleton *et al.* (1943) being used to detect diacetyl.

Carbohydrate fermentation. Fermentation of sugars differentiates the leuconostocs into six groups, three of which appear to be closely related and to form the species *Leuc. mesenteroides*.

Dextran production. This is characteristic of many strains of *Leuc. mesenteroides* and *Leuc. dextranicum* and is observed by the production of large mucoid colonies on a medium containing 5% sucrose (Garvie, 1960).

Pediococcus

The media and methods of Gunther and White (1961) and Coster and White (1964) are used, except that MRS broth (de Man *et al.*, 1960) is recommended instead of tomato-juice broth for general cultivation and as a basal medium. The classification of Pedersen (1949), Gunther and White (1961), Coster and White (1964) and Deibel and Niven (1960) is used to

TABLE 3. Physiological characteristics of members of the genus *Pediococcus*

	P. cere-viseae	Gunther and White group III	P. parvulus	P. dam-nosus	P. halo-philus	P. homari or Aero-coccus viridans
Growth at 37°C.	+	+	+	−	+	+
Growth at 45°C.	+	−	−	−	−	−
Growth at pH 4·4	+	−	+	+	−	−
Growth at pH 8·6	+	−	−	−	+	+
Growth in 10% NaCl	sl	−	−	−	+	+
Growth on Rogosa medium	+	+	+	+	−	−
Catalase reaction	±	−	−	−	−	−
Requiring 5% NcCl for growth	−	−	−	−	+	−
NH₃ from arginine	+ usually	−	−	−	+	−
*AMC from glucose	+	−	−	±	±	−
Acid from:						
sucrose	−	−	−	−	+	+
arabinose	+	−	−	−	+	−
raffinose	−	−	−	−	−	+
sorbitol	−	−	−	−	+	−
dextrin	−	+	−	−	−	−
maltose	+	±	+	−	+	+
Lactic acid	DL	L(+)	DL	DL	L(+)	L(+)

* AMC = acetyl methyl carbinol.

differentiate the species (Table 3). Nakagawa and Kitahara (1959) have suggested a somewhat different scheme of classification of the pediococci, based on similar tests, but in which the name *P. cereviseae* is applied to very different organisms from those described here. Whilst this scheme may have some merits and has been used by some workers, the use of two such different systems can lead only to confusion. The classification of *P. cereviseae* in our table is that in general use. A description of *P. cereviseae* has been submitted to the International Committee of Bacterial Nomenclature by Gunther and White (1962) and until this body has expressed an official opinion it seems wiser to use the generally accepted nomenclature.

There is some doubt as to whether the aerococci should be included in the genus *Pediococcus*. However, the fact that they are fermentative and unable to grow in the absence of carbohydrate (Deibel and Niven, 1960; Garvie, unpublished data) justifies their inclusion here.

Requirement of P. cereviseae for folinic acid. Many strains of *P. cereviseae* have an absolute requirement for folinic acid. Strains of pediococci grown in a tryptone broth are subcultured into the casein hydrolysate medium of Eigen and Shockman (1963) and into the same medium without folinic acid. A requirement for folinic acid is denoted by absence of growth in the folinic acid deficient medium after three serial transfers.

Serological tests. Gunther and White (1961) and Coster and White (1964) have detected specific precipitins characteristic for different groups of pediococci. This may be a useful aid in identification, although we ourselves have no experience with it.

Absence of cytochrome-containing respiratory systems. Many strains of *P. cereviseae* when grown on a low sugar containing medium produce a "pseudocatalase" which decomposes hydrogen peroxide, but differs from catalase in being insensitive to cyanide and to azide and not containing a haem prosthetic group (Delwiche, 1961; Johnston and Delwiche, 1965; Whittenbury, 1960; Whittenbury, 1964). However, Deibel and Evans (1960) have shown that cytochrome-containing systems can be detected in bacteria by a benzidine test for iron porphyrins, and that this clearly differentiates lactic acid bacteria (including pseudocatalase-producing strains) which do not possess a cytochrome system from morphologically related organisms which do.

Organisms are grown on any suitable nutrient agar, the plate is then flooded with benzidine hydrochloride solution, followed by the addition of an equal volume of 5% hydrogen peroxide. If iron-porphyrin compounds are present in the culture a blue colour develops in the microbial growth, which otherwise remains colourless.

A few strains of leuconostocs and lactobacilli may also produce pseudo-catalase, and these also give a negative reaction with the benzidine test.

Lactobacillus

This genus was subdivided by Orla Jensen (1919, 1943) into three main groups, *Thermobacterium, Streptobacterium* and *Betabacterium*, by their growth temperatures and end-products of carbohydrate fermentation. Each contains a number of species (Table 4). Whilst the names of these subgenera

TABLE 4. Physiological characteristics of lactobacilli
showing the three main groups and the species which they contain

Homofermentative		Heterofermentative
carbohydrates fermented to lactic acid		carbohydrates fermented to lactic acid + volatile acid + CO_2
Thermobacterium growth at 45°C.+ growth at 15°C.− L. *helveticus* L. *jugurti* L. *bulgaricus* L. *lactis* L. *acidophilus* L. *leichmannii* L. *delbrueckii* L. *salivarius*	*Streptobacterium* growth at 45°C.∓ growth at 15°C.+ L. *casei* L. *plantarum*	*Betabacterium* L. *fermenti* L. *buchneri* L. *brevis* L. *cellobiosus* L. *viridescens*

are not valid according to Bergey's Manual (Breed *et al.*, 1957), they are at present recognized as a useful subdivision of the genus *Lactobacillus*. The species within these groups can be differentiated by means of biochemical, physiological and serological characteristics and by their vitamin requirements. Recent general reviews of this work are given by Rogosa *et al.* (1953); Rogosa and Sharpe (1959); Davis (1960) and Sharpe (1962).

Physiological tests

The MRS medium of de Man, Rogosa and Sharpe (1960) is used for general cultivation of strains, determination of growth temperatures, and in a modified form as the basal medium for biochemical tests. The methods referred to by Sharpe (1962) are used.

Carbohydrate fermentation. Inocula of cultures into test substrate, using washed organisms, must be from vigorously growing strains. The basal medium recommended is MRS broth with glucose and meat extract omitted and indicator added, the final pH being 6·4.

Most carbohydrates can be added to the medium before heating, but mannose, xylose and maltose, which decompose on heating, should be

TABLE 5. Differentiating characteristics in the thermobacteria (data taken from Rogosa and Sharpe, 1959)

Species of *Lactobacillus*	Presence of granules	Growth at 15°C	Growth at 45°C	% acid in milk	Lactic acid configuration	NH₃ from arginine	Aesculin hydrolysis	Amygdalin	Cellobiose	Galactose	Lactose	Maltose	Mannitol	Melibiose	Salicin	Sorbitol	Sucrose	Trehalose	Serological group	Riboflavin	Pyridoxal	Folic acid	Vitamin B₁₂	Thymidine
helveticus	−	−	+	2·7	DL	−	−	−	−	+	+	+	−	−	−	−	−	±	A	+	+	−	−	−
jugurti	−	−	±	2·7	DL	−	−	−	−	+	+	−	−	−	−	−	−	±	A	+	+	−	−	−
bulgaricus	+	−	+	1·7	D(−)	−	−	−	−	+	+	−	−	−	−	−	−	−	E	+	−	−	−	−
lactis	+	−	+	1·7	D(−)	−	−	−	−	+	+	+	−	−	+	−	+	+	E	+	−	−	±	−
acidophilus	−	−	+	0·8	DL	−	+	+	+	+	+	+	−	±	+	−	+	+	·	+	−	+	±	−
leichmannii	+	−	±	0	D(−)	±	+	+	+	−	±	+	−	−	+	−	+	+	·	−	−	+	+	−
delbrueckii	−	−	+	0	L(+)	±	−	+	−	±	−	±	−	−	−	−	+	−	·	+	+	−	−	+
salivarius	−	−	+	0·9	L(+) & DL	−	±	+	−	+	+	+	+	+	+	+	+	+	G	+	−	+	−	−

* + = requirement; − = no requirement.
None ferment arabinose, xylose, melezitose. None require thiamine for growth. None produce CO₂ from glucose.
. = grouping antiserum could not be prepared.

TABLE 6. Differentiating characteristics in the streptobacteria (data taken from Rogosa and Sharpe, 1959)

Species of *Lactobacillus*	Microscopic appearance	Growth at 15°C	Growth at 45°C	% acid in milk	Lactic acid configuration	Growth in 0.4% Teepol	Fermentation of:							Serological group	Nutritional requirements*	
							Arabinose	Lactose	Melibiose	Raffinose	Rhamnose	Sucrose	Xylose		Pyridoxal	Folic acid
casei var. *casei*	Usually small G + rods in chains	+	±	1·2–1·5	L(+)	–	–	+	–	–	–	+	–	B, C	+	+
casei var. *rhamnosus*	Usually small G + rods in chains	+	+	1·2–1·5	L(+)	–	–	+	–	–	+	–	–	C	+	+
casei var. *alactosus*	Usually small G + rods in chains	+	–	0	L(+)	–	–	–	–	–	–	+	–	†B, C	+	+
plantarum	Small or medium Single G + rods	+	±	0·3–1·2	DL	+	±	+	+	+	±	+	±	D	–	–

* + = requirement; – = no requirement.
† Most strains fall into group B.
All hydrolyse aesculin, ferment amygdalin, cellobiose, galactose, fructose, maltose, mannitol, salicin, sorbitol. None require thiamine for growth. None give CO_2 from glucose.

added as Seitz-filtered solutions after sterilization of the basal medium. By means of sugar fermentations seven species can be differentiated among the thermobacteria (Table 5). Two species, however, *L. jugurti* and *L. bulgaricus*, have identical fermentation reactions and must be distinguished by other tests. Fermentation of melibiose and raffinose and sometimes xylose distinguish *L. plantarum* from *L. casei* (Table 6). With the betabacteria the reactions are less clear cut in the different species. However, *L. fermenti* seldom ferments the pentoses, only *L. buchneri* ferments melezitose, only *L. cellobiosus* ferments cellobiose and *L. viridescens* is relatively inactive.

Production of NH3 from arginine. The test is very useful as a confirmatory test in distinguishing homofermentative from heterofermentative lactobacilli, as almost all of the latter hydrolyse arginine (Table 7), whilst the

TABLE 7. Differentiating characteristics in the betabacteria
(data taken from Rogosa and Sharpe, 1959)

Species of Lactobacillus	Growth at 15°C	Growth at 45°C	Aesculin hydrolysis	Growth in 0.4% Teepol	NH₃ from arginine	Fermentation of: Arabinose	Cellobiose	Melezitose	Melibiose	Raffinose	Trehalose	Xylose	Serological group	Nutritional requirements* Riboflavin	Pyridoxal	Folic acid
fermenti	−	+	−	−	+	−	−	−	±	+	±	−	F	−	−	−
buchneri	+	±	±	+	+	+	−	+	+	+	−	±	E	±	−	−
brevis	+	−	±	+	+	+	−	−	+	−	−	+	E	−	−	+
cellobiosus	+	−	+	+	+	−	+	−	+	+	+	±	.	−	−	−
viridescens	+	−	−	+	−	−	−	−	−	−	±	−	.	+	−	−

* + = requirement; − = no requirement.
All require thiamine. None ferment amygdalin, rhamnose, sorbitol. All ferment maltose. All produce DL-lactic acid. All give CO₂ from glucose.
. = no grouping antisera prepared.

thermobacteria and streptobacteria do not. The concentration of glucose used in the test medium is important: with a high concentration (2%) only heterofermentative strains produce NH₃. With a lower concentration some strains of *L. plantarum* may also produce NH₃, and the test loses its significance for distinguishing these groups.

The ability to split aesculin can be demonstrated by the formation of a black precipitate in the presence of ferric ammonium citrate (Naylor and Sharpe, 1958), or by the quenching of the fluorescence of the aesculin (Rogosa and Sharpe, 1959). This test is useful for distinguishing the species in the thermobacteria and to some extent in the betabacteria.

Serological tests

Many lactobacilli can be classified by means of their acid-soluble, heat-stable antigens into groups compatible with their cultural and physiological characteristics (Sharpe, 1955; Sharpe and Wheater, 1957). Ring precipitin tests (Sharpe, 1955) or slide gel diffusion tests (Mansi, 1958), similar to those described for the streptococci, are used to detect these reactions. By these tests *L. jugurti* and *L. bulgaricus* can be differentiated among the thermobacteria (Table 5); two serological groups can be distinguished in the species *L. casei* (Table 6), and *L. fermenti* has a different group antigen from *L. brevis* and *L. buchneri* (Table 7). For some species no serological group has yet been assigned, because it has not been possible to prepare antisera which demonstrate grouping antigens for them.

Nutritional tests

The nutritional requirements of lactobacilli also differentiate them (Rogosa, Tittsler and Geib, 1947; Rogosa, Franklin and Perry, 1961) and can be used to confirm their identity. The media and methods of Rogosa, Franklin and Perry (1961) are used. The homofermentative lactobacilli do not require thiamine for growth, whilst the heterofermentative strains do. Other requirements distinguish six species among the thermobacteria, differentiate *L. casei* from *L. plantarum*, and differentiate some species of betabacteria (Tables 5–7).

Correlation between methods

It can be seen that there is a good correlation between the different methods of identification. Usually it is possible to identify species by physiological and biochemical characteristics alone, if facilities are not available for other methods to be used.

As with the streptococci, strains are often encountered, especially among the streptobacteria, which cannot yet be identified.

Leuconostocs and Heterofermentative Lactobacilli

Leuconostoc mesenteroides and *Leuc. dextranicum* may frequently occur in the same habitat as the heterofermentative *Lactobacillus brevis*. As they will all grow on the selective acetate media of Rogosa *et al.* (1951) and Mabbitt and Zielinska (1956), they are likely to be isolated together, and may not be readily distinguished morphologically, as they can all occur as coccobacilli (Perry and Sharpe, 1960). However, the leuconostocs can be differentiated by their ability to ferment trehalose, but not to hydrolyse arginine, and by forming D(−) lactic acid, whilst *L. brevis* does not ferment trehalose, hydrolyses arginine and forms DL lactic acid (Tables 2 and 7).

References

ABD-EL-MALEK, Y., & GIBSON, T. (1948). Studies in the bacteriology of milk. 1. The streptococci of milk. *J. Dairy Res.*, **15**, 233.

BARNES, E. M. (1956). Tetrazolium reduction as a means of differentiating *Streptococcus faecalis* from *Streptococcus faecium*. *J. gen. Microbiol.*, **14**, 57.

BREED, R. S., MURRAY, E. G. D., & SMITH, N. R. (1957). *Bergey's Manual of Determinative Bacteriology*, 7th ed. London: Baillière, Tindall and Cox.

COSTER, E., & WHITE, H. R. (1964). Further studies of the Genus *Pediococcus*. *J. gen. Microbiol.*, **37**, 15.

CRUIKSHANK, R. (1960). *Mackie and McCartney's Handbook of Bacteriology*, 10th ed. London: Livingstone.

DAVIS, J. G. (1960). The lactobacilli—I. *Progr. in Indust. Microbiol.*, **2**, 3.

DEIBEL, R. H. (1964). The group D streptococci. *Bact. Rev.*, **28**, 330.

DEIBEL, R. H., & EVANS, J. B. (1960). Modified benzidine test for the detection of cytochrome containing respiratory systems in micro-organisms. *J. Bact.*, **79**, 356.

DEIBEL, R. H., & NIVEN, C. F., JR. (1960). Comparative study of *Gaffkya homari*, *Aerococcus viridans*, tetrad-forming cocci from meat curing brines, and the genus Pediococcus. *J. Bact.*, **79**, 175.

DELWICHE, E. A. (1961). Catalase of *Pediococcus cereviseae*. *J. Bact.*, **81**, 416.

DE MAN, J. C., ROGOSA, M., & SHARPE, M. E. (1960). A medium for the cultivation of lactobacilli, *J. appl. Bact.*, **23**, 130.

DUNICAN, L. K., & SEELEY, H. W. (1962). Starch hydrolysis by *Streptococcus equinus*. *J. Bact.*, **83**, 264.

EGGLETON, P., ELSDEN, S. R., & GOUGH, N. (1943). The estimation of creatine and of diacetyl. *Biochem. J.* **37**, 526.

EIGEN, E., & SHOCKMAN, G. D. (1963). *Analytical Microbiology*. Ed. Kavanagh. New York and London: Academic Press, p. 467.

FULLER, A. T. (1938). The formamide method for the extraction of polysaccharides from haemolytic streptococci. *Brit. J. exp. Path.*, **19**, 130.

GARVIE, E. I. (1960). The genus *Leuconostoc* and its nomenclature. *J. Dairy Res.*, **27**, 283.

GIBSON, T., & ABD-EL-MALEK, Y. (1945). The formation of CO_2 by lactic acid bacteria and *Bacillus licheniformis* and a cultural method of detecting the process. *J. Dairy Res.*, **14**, 35.

GUNSALUS, I. C. (1947). Products of anaerobic glycerol fermentation by *Streptococcus faecalis*. *J. Bact.*, **54**, 239.

GUNTHER, H. L. (1959). Mode of division of pediococci. *Nature, Lond.*, **183**, 903.

GUNTHER, H. L., & WHITE, H. R. (1961). The cultural and physiological characters of the pediococci. *J. gen. Microbiol.*, **26**, 185.

GUNTHER, H. L., & WHITE, H. R. (1962). Proposed designation of a neotype strain of *Pediococcus cereviseae* Balcke. *Int. Bull. bact. Nomencl.* **12**, 185.

HUGH, R., & LEIFSON, E. (1953). The taxonomic significance of fermentative versus oxidative metabolism of carbohydrates by various Gram negative bacteria. *J. Bact.*, **66**, 24.

JOHNSTON, M. A., & DELWICHE, E. A. (1965). Distribution and characteristics of the catalases of Lactobacillaceae. *J. Bact.*, **90**, 347.

LANCEFIELD, R. C. (1933). A serological differentiation of human and other groups of haemolytic streptococci. *J. exp. Med.*, **57**, 571.

MABBITT, L. A., & ZIELINSKA, M. (1956). The use of a selective medium for the enumeration of lactobacilli in Cheddar cheese. *J. appl. Bact.*, **19,** 95.

MANSI, W. (1958). Slide gel diffusion precipitation test. *Nature, Lond.*, **181,** 1289.

MEDREK, T. F., & BARNES, E. M. (1962). The physiological and serological properties of *Streptococcus bovis* and related organisms isolated from cattle and sheep. *J. appl. Bact.*, **25,** 169.

NAKAGAWA, A., & KITAHARA, K. (1959). Taxonomic studies on the genus *Pediococcus. J. gen. appl. Microbiol., Tokyo,* **5,** 95.

NAYLOR, J., & SHARPE, M. E. (1958). Lactobacilli in Cheddar cheese. I. The use of selective media for isolation and serological typing for identification. *J. Dairy Res.*, **25,** 92.

ORLA JENSEN, S. (1919). *The Lactic Acid Bacteria.* Copenhagen: Andr. Fred Host and Son.

ORLA JENSEN, S. (1943). *The Lactic Acid Bacteria.* Copenhagen: Einar Munksgaard.

PEDERSON, C. S. (1949). The genus *Pediococcus. Bact. Rev.*, **13,** 225.

PERRY, K. D., & SHARPE, M. E. (1960). Lactobacilli in raw milk and in Cheddar cheese. *J. Dairy Res.*, **27,** 267.

REITER, B., & MØLLER-MADSEN, A. (1963). Cheese and butter starters. *J. Dairy Res.*, **30,** 419.

ROGOSA, M., FRANKLIN, J. G., & PERRY, K. D. (1961). Correlation of the vitamin requirements with cultural and biochemical characters of *Lactobacillus* spp. *J. gen. Microbiol.*, **25,** 473.

ROGOSA, M., MITCHELL, J. A., & WISEMAN, R. F. (1951). A selective medium for the isolation of oral and faecal lactobacilli. *J. Bact.*, **62,** 132.

ROGOSA, M., & SHARPE, M. E. (1959). An approach to the classification of the lactobacilli. *J. appl. Bact.*, **22,** 329.

ROGOSA, M., TITTSLER, R. P., & GEIB, D. S. (1947). Correlation of vitamin requirements and cultural and biochemical characteristics of the genus *Lactobacillus. J. Bact.*, **54,** 13.

ROGOSA, M., WISEMAN, R. F., MITCHELL, J. A., DISRAELY, M. N., & BEAMAN, A. J. (1953). Species differentiation of oral lactobacilli from man including descriptions of *Lactobacillus salivarius* nov. spec. and *Lactobacillus cellobiosus* nov. spec. *J. Bact.*, **65,** 681.

SHARPE, M. E. (1955). A serological classification of lactobacilli. *J. gen. Microbiol.*, **12,** 107.

SHARPE, M. E. (1962). Taxonomy of the lactobacilli. *Dairy Sci. Abstr.*, **24,** 109.

SHARPE, M. E. (1964). Serological types of *Streptococcus faecalis* and its varieties and their cell wall type antigen. *J. gen. Microbiol.*, **36,** 151.

SHARPE, M. E., & FEWINS, B. G. (1960). Serological typing of strains of *Streptococcus faecium* and unclassified Group D streptococci from canned hams and pig intestines. *J. gen. Microbiol.*, **23,** 621.

SHARPE, M. E., & WHEATER, D. M. (1957). *Lactobacillus helveticus. J. gen. Microbiol.*, **16,** 676.

SHATTOCK, P. M. F. (1949). The streptococci of Group D; the serological grouping of *Streptococcus bovis* and observations on serologically refractory Group D strains. *J. gen. Microbiol.*, **3,** 80.

SHATTOCK, P. M. F. (1962). Enterococci. Ed. Ayres, J. C., Kraft, A. A., Snyder, H. E., & Walker, H. W. *Chemical and biological hazards in food.* Ames: Iowa State University Press, p. 303.

SHERMAN, J. M. (1937). The Streptococci. *Bact. Rev.*, **1**, 3.

SKADHAUGE, K. (1950). *Studies on enterococci with special reference to the serological properties*. Copenhagen: Einar Munksgaards Forlag.

SKERMAN, V. B. D. (1959). *A guide to the identification of the genera of bacteria*. Baltimore: Williams and Wilkins.

SMITH, D. G., & SHATTOCK, P. M. F. (1962). The serological grouping of *Streptococcus equinus*. *J. gen. Microbiol.*, **29**, 731.

WHITTENBURY, R. (1960). Two types of catalase like activity. *Nature, Lond.*, **187**, 433.

WHITTENBURY, R. (1964). Hydrogen peroxide formation and catalase activity in the lactic acid bacteria. *J. gen. Microbiol.*, **35**, 13.

WILSON, G. S., & MILES, A. A. (1955). *Topley and Wilson's Principles of Bacteriology and Immunity*, 4th ed. p. 451. London: Arnold.

Colonial Morphology and Fluorescent Labelled Antibody Staining in the Identification of Species of the Genus *Clostridium**

IRENE BATTY AND P. D. WALKER

The Wellcome Research Laboratories, Beckenham, Kent, England

A recent modification of the McIntosh and Fildes jar (McIntosh and Fildes, 1916) which utilizes a catalyst of palladianized alumina, active at room temperature (Heller, 1954), provides the simplest and most convenient way of isolating and obtaining surface cultures of anaerobes. By the use of appropriate media in which suitable indicator systems can be incorporated (Willis, 1960) many species of clostridia can readily be identified by this method. Nevertheless, there still exists opposition to its use, mainly because either it is allegedly difficult to use and requires special apparatus or the method only allows the growth of those anaerobes which are relatively easy to culture. The first view is taken by the French school (Prevot, personal communication), who prefer the use of Veillon tubes for isolation of anaerobic organisms in pure culture, and by a number of other workers, e.g. Shank (1963), who offer alternative techniques such as plastic films. The second view is taken by some Canadian workers (Fredette, 1956). Many of these techniques are open to the serious objection that many anaerobes have the property of forming a thin spreading layer between surfaces, e.g. glass/agar and plastic/agar, a property which makes the resolution of mixtures of anaerobes extremely difficult. It is frequently forgotten that many aerobes are difficult to cultivate on plates unless the ordinary medium is suitably supplemented, and that failure to grow is not necessarily a result of culture on a surface.

In the present paper the colonial appearances of a number of anaerobes which are routinely examined in our laboratories are described. Many of these are usually described as difficult to grow, and it is hoped that some of the points which will emerge from these descriptions will be useful to those working in other fields.

The use of fluorescent labelled antisera for the identification of clostridia has previously only been investigated with *Clostridium botulinum* (Bulatova

* Reprinted from *J. appl. Bacteriol.* **28**, 1, 112.

and Kabanova, 1960; Kalitina, 1960) and *Clostridium welchii (perfringens)* (Geck and Szanto, 1961). The method, where applicable, appears to have many advantages in the identification of clostridia, and some recent work will be reviewed.

Materials and Methods

Organisms

The following organisms were used: *Cl. welchii (perfringens)* (CN 5385, CN 5386); *Cl. tetani* (CN 655); *Cl. sporogenes* (CN 642); *Cl. bifermentans* (CN 1617); *Cl. sordellii* (CN 1620); *Cl. botulinum*, type A (NCTC 2916), type B (CN 5009), type C (CN 4946), type D (CN 4947) and type E (E20 Dolman); *Cl. novyi (oedematiens)*, type A (CN 1496), type B (CN 755) and type D (CN 3629); *Cl. chauvoei* (CN 5002); *Cl. septicum* (CN 5293); *Cl. histolyticum* (CN 647) and *Cl. tertium* (CN 4603).

Media

Normal blood agar: nutrient broth containing 1·8% of agar* 75 parts; pancreatic autodigest 25 parts; horse blood 5 parts, by volume.

Stiff blood agar: as above but containing 3% of agar.

Cl. chauvoei *medium*. Nutrient broth containing 1·8% of agar 75 parts; 50% glucose 2 parts; liver extract 3 parts; sheep's blood 5 parts, by volume.

Cl. novyi *medium*. Nutrient broth containing 3% of agar 75 parts; pancreatic autodigest 10 parts; 10% Lab-Lemco 5 parts; 10% proteose peptone 5 parts; 50% glucose 1 part; horse blood 5 parts, by volume.

Plates of the above media were poured and inoculated as soon as dry with a loopful of an overnight culture in Robertson's meat broth. The inoculated plates were immediately transferred to an anaerobic jar and incubated for appropriate periods before examination. The colonies were photographed under a Vickers projection microscope (Vickers Ltd), the angle of incidence of the light being varied to reveal their shape and surface texture. The illumination was either by tungsten light or carbon arc, depending on the configuration of the colony.

Fluorescent staining. The preparation of antisera, conjugation procedures and staining techniques were as described in Batty and Walker (1963*a, b*).

Results

Surface culture

In the several plates, the magnification of the organisms and colonies has been standardized at ×2000 and ×6, respectively. The appearance of

* New Zealand agar ≡ 1·6 times Oxoid No. 3 is used throughout.

colonies at this magnification corresponds approximately to those seen with a hand lens. The photographs are designed to bring out surface details and no attempt has been made to show haemolysis, which in many cases is an important ancillary factor in identifying the organism.

Cl. welchii (perfringens)

The morphological appearance is shown (Fig. 1 (a)); spores are rarely seen and the typical appearance is of short Gram-positive rods with square ends. The characteristic smooth, circular, convex colonies with an entire margin are shown (Fig. 1 (b)). Occasionally rough colonies are found (Fig. 1 (c)). There appears to be little correlation between colonial morphology and the various toxigenic types of this organism.

Cl. tetani

The typical drumstick appearance is seen on smears (Fig. 2 (a)). On ordinary agar plates, isolated surface colonies are difficult to obtain, because Cl. tetani commonly spreads as a fine rhizoidal film over the surface. Isolated colonies can be obtained, however, on stiff agar plates (Fig. 2 (b)). The rhizoidal edges can be seen clearly, but the colony remains quite discrete.

Cl. sporogenes

This organism is a common contaminant. It produces oval spores which swell the sporangium (Fig. 2 (c)). The colonies are umbonate with an opaque greyish-white centre, and a flattened irregular periphery (Fig. 2 (d)).

Cl. bifermentans/Cl. sordellii

These two species are regarded as distinct by some workers and as varieties of the same species by others (Tataki and Huet, 1953; Ellner and Green, 1963; Smith, 1955). A comprehensive treatment is to be found in Brooks and Epps (1959), who draw attention to the characters which can be used to separate Cl. bifermentans from Cl. sordellii. Morphologically the two organisms are indistinguishable; both are large rods with cylindrical spores causing little swelling of the sporangium (Figs. 3 (a) and (c)). There are, however, slight differences in appearance on surface culture, colonies of Cl. bifermentans being in general low, convex and with an entire margin (Fig. 3 (b)), whilst those of Cl. sordellii usually have a markedly irregular margin and tend to follow the line of the streak (Fig. 3 (d)).

Cl. botulinum, types A, B, C, D and E

In the current edition of Bergey's Manual (1957), the name Cl. botulinum is reserved for the non proteolytic types C, D and E, while the name Cl.

IMM–D

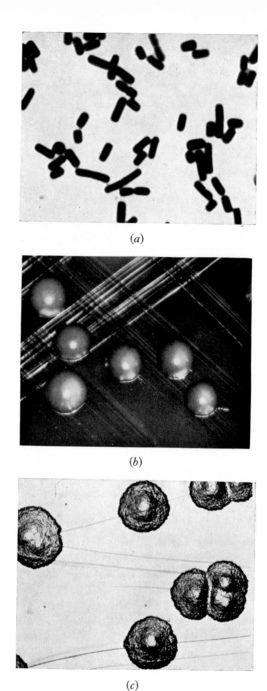

(a)

(b)

(c)

Fig. 1. Morphological appearances of *Cl. welchii* (a) from a surface colony 24 h old
(×2000); (b) smooth surface colonies 24 h old (×6); (c) rough surface colonies 24 h
old (×6).

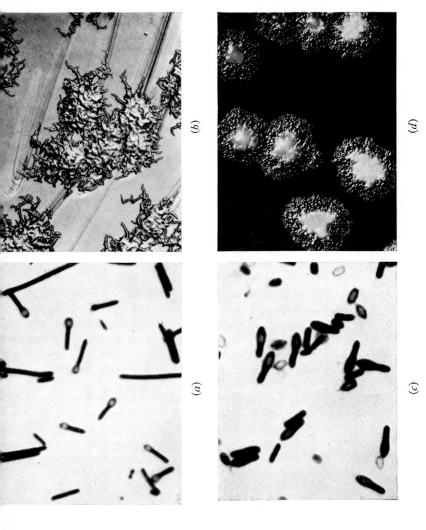

FIG. 2. Morphological appearances of *Cl. tetani* (*a*) from a surface colony 48 h old (×2000); (*b*) surface colony 48 h old (×6); and of *Cl. sporogenes* (*c*) from a surface colony 24 h old (×2000); (*d*) surface colonies 24 h old (×6).

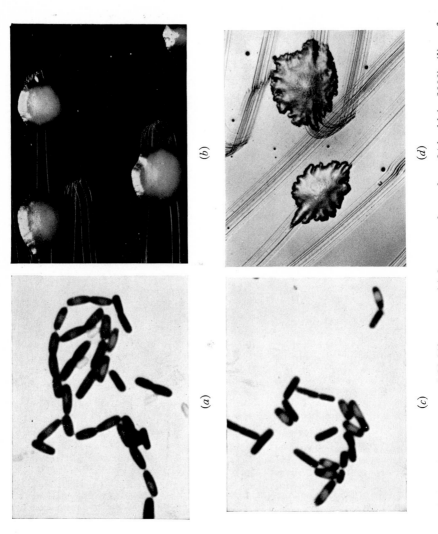

FIG. 3. Morphological appearances of *Cl. bifermentans* (*a*) from a surface colony 24 h old (× 2000); (*b*) surface colonies 24 h old (× 6); and of *Cl. sordellii* (*c*) from a surface colony 24 h old (× 2000); (*d*) surface colonies 24 h old (× 6).

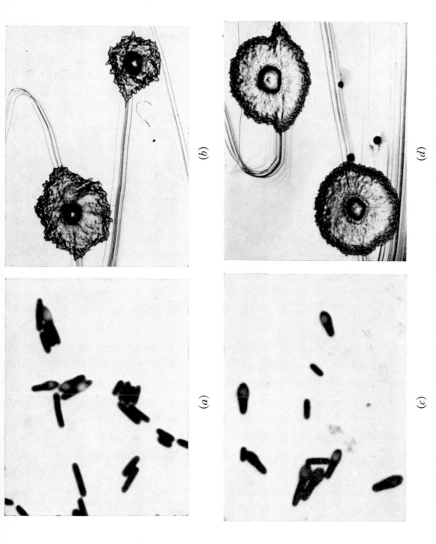

FIG. 4. Morphological appearances of *Cl. botulinum* type A (*a*) from a surface colony 48 h old (×2000); (*b*) surface colonies 48 h old (×6); and of type B (*c*) from a surface colony 48 h old (×2000); (*d*) surface colonies 48 h old (×6).

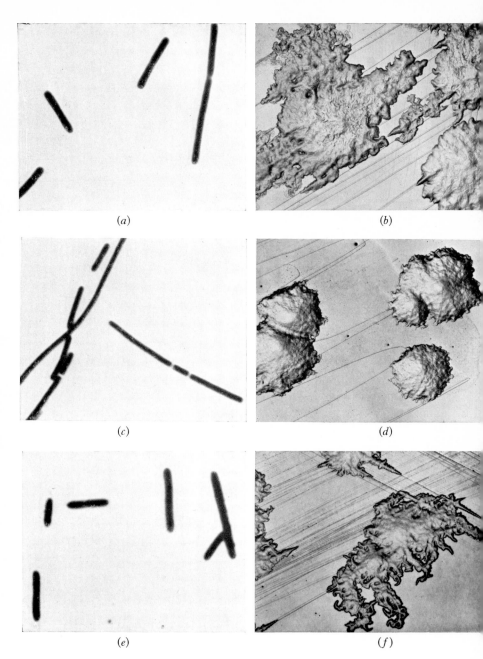

FIG. 5. Morphological appearances of *Cl. botulinum* type C (*a*) from a surface colony 48 h old (×2000); (*b*) surface colonies 48 h old (×6); of type D (*c*) from a surface colony 48 h old (×2000); (*d*) surface colonies 48 h old (×6); and of type E (*e*) from a surface colony 48 h old (×2000); (*f*) 48 h old (×6) surface colonies.

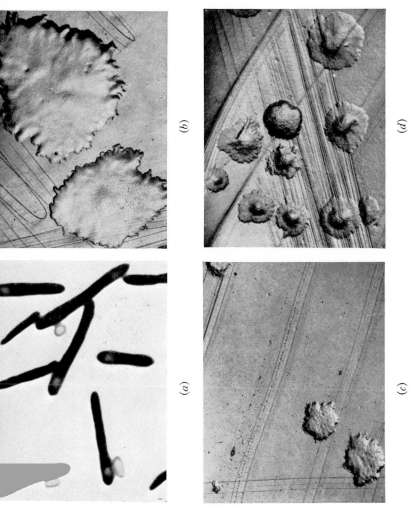

(a)

(b)

(c)

(d)

FIG. 6. Morphological appearances of *Cl. novyii* type A (*a*) from a surface colony 48 h old (× 2000); (*b*) surface colonies 48 h old (× 6); of type B (*c*) surface colonies 48 h old (× 2000); and of type D (*d*) surface colonies 48 h old (× 6).

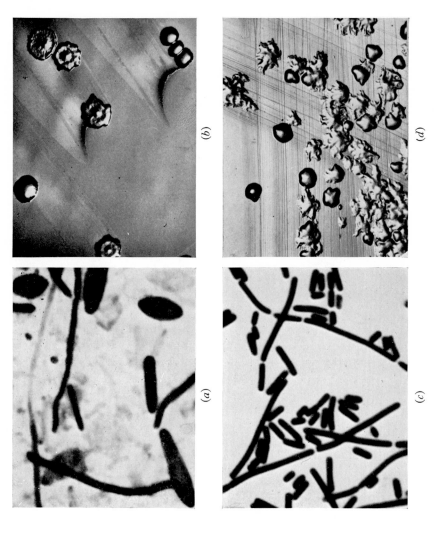

Fig. 7. Morphological appearances of *Cl. chauvoei* (*a*) from a surface colony 48 h old (× 2000); (*b*) surface colonies rough and smooth 48 h old (× 6); and of *Cl. septicum* (*c*) from a surface colony 24 h old (× 2000); (*d*) surface colonies rough and smooth

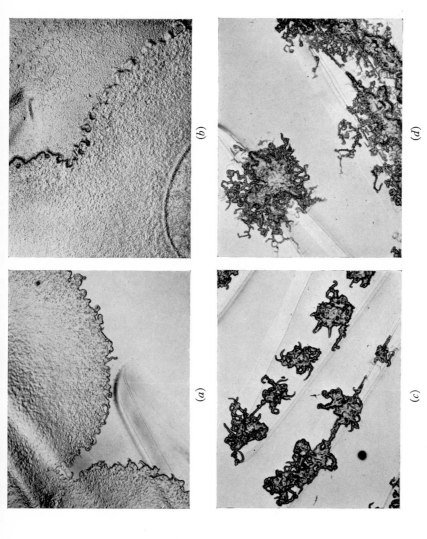

FIG. 8. Morphological appearances of *Cl. septicum* (*a*) a surface colony 24 h old on ordinary agar (×6); (*b*) surface colony 48 h old on ordinary agar (×6); (*c*) surface colonies on 24 h old stiff agar (×6); (*d*) surface colonies on stiff agar 48 h old (×6).

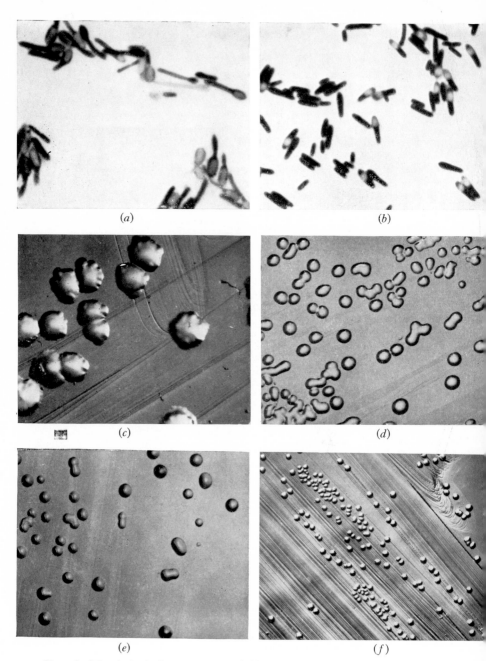

FIG. 9. Morphological appearances of *Cl. tertium* (a) from a surface colony 24 h old ($\times 2000$); (c) surface colonies anaerobic 24 h old ($\times 6$); (e) surface colonies aerobic 24 h old ($\times 6$); and of *Cl. histolyticum* (b) from a surface colony 24 h old ($\times 2000$); (d) surface colonies anaerobic 24 h old ($\times 6$); (f) surface colonies aerobic 24 h old ($\times 6$).

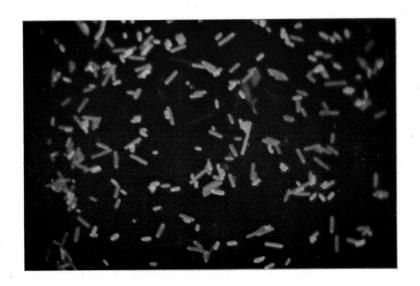

FIG. 10. A smear of a mixed *Cl. septicum* and *Cl. chauvoei* culture stained with a mixture of fluorescein isothiocyanate labelled *Cl. septicum* antiserum and lissamine rhodamine B.200 *Cl. chauvoei* labelled antiserum.

parabotulinum is used to distinguish the proteolytic types A and B; the recently isolated type F is also included in this latter group. These differences in metabolic activity are reflected in the morphology and colonial appearance of the organisms. Both *Cl. botulinum* type A and type B are morphologically similar and produce oval spores swelling the sporangium (Figs. 4 (*a*) and (*c*)). Both have umbonate colonies with a granular periphery and irregular margin (Figs. 4 (*b*) and (*d*)).

Cl. botulinum types C, D and E resemble each other both morphologically and culturally, though in this latter aspect types C and D are more fastidious, but they do grow on the medium prescribed for *Cl. novyii*. As Figs. 5 (*a*), (*c*) and (*e*) show, all three are large bacilli giving rise to spores only infrequently. The colonies of the usual toxigenic wild types are large with a granular surface and a rhizoidal margin (Figs. 5 (*b*), (*d*) and (*f*)). Colonies of the various mutants described by Dolman (1957) are not shown.

Cl. novyii (oedematiens)

This species is divisible into four types, A, B, C and D. *Cl. novyii* type D is probably one of the most fastidious of the pathogenic clostridia. The organisms are large Gram-positive rods with oval spores (Fig. 6 (*a*)). Colonies of type A are flat with a finely granular surface and an irregular edge (Fig. 6 (*b*)), whilst those of type B, although similar, are smaller (Fig. 6 (*c*)) and those of type D are more umbonate, with entire irregular margins (Fig. 6 (*d*)).

Cl. chauveoei/Cl. septicum

Clostridium chauvoei and *Cl. septicum* are two species which though very similar morphologically can be distinguished culturally. Both organisms are pleomorphic and this quality is well illustrated in the case of *Cl. chauvoei* (Plate 7 (*a*) and of *Cl. septicum* (Fig. 7 (*c*)). *Cl. chauvoei* is a more fastidious organism than *Cl. septicum* and to ensure growth the special medium already described should be used. The majority of colonies of *Cl. chauvoei* are umbonate with a raised lip, but occasionally smooth colonies are seen (Fig. 7 (*b*)) which resemble the smooth colonies of *Cl. septicum* (Fig. 7 (*d*)), where some smooth colonies can be seen amongst the more usual spreading rhizoidal colonies.

If *Cl. septicum* is grown on 1·8% agar, like *Cl. tetani*, it spreads over the surface. After 24 h the spreading edge can be clearly seen (Fig. 8 (*a*)), but after 48 h the growth has completely covered the surface of the agar plate (Fig. 8 (*b*)). If, however, the same strain is grown on 3% agar discrete rhizoidal colonies can be seen after 24 h, which increase in size during the next 24 h, but remain discrete (Figs. 8 (*c*) and (*d*)).

Cl. tertium/Cl. histolyticum

These two organisms are micro-aerophilic. Morphologically *Cl. tertium* has characteristic large terminal oval spores which swell the sporangium (Fig. 9 (*a*)). When grown anaerobically it produces smooth round colonies with a crenated edge (Fig. 9 (*c*)). The colonies which develop under aerobic conditions are much smaller (Fig. 9 (*e*)).

Cl. histolyticum is widely distributed and is strongly proteolytic. It also produces oval spores which swell the sporangium (Fig. 9 (*b*)). The colonies are opaque and greyish-white with entire margins (Fig. 9 (*d*)). Colonies grown aerobically are again much smaller (Fig. 9 (*f*)) than those grown anaerobically.

Fluorescent staining

In a series of papers (Batty and Walker (1963*a*, *b*, 1964); Walker and Batty (1964); Batty *et al.* (1964)), the fluorescent labelled antibody staining technique and its application as a diagnostic aid are discussed. The main conclusions are summarized as follows.

Cl. septicum/chauvoei

Twenty-two strains of *Cl. septicum* collected from all over the world could be divided into two groups on the basis of "O" agglutination and fluorescent staining, whilst twenty-six strains of *Cl. chauvoei*, again collected from all over the world, fell into a single group both by the "O" agglutination or by fluorescent staining. Neither species showed any cross reaction in "O" agglutination or by fluorescent staining. Strains of both species could be identified in a single smear by labelling the *Cl. septicum* antiserum with fluorescein isothiocyanate (green fluorescence) and the *Cl. chauvoei* antiserum with lissamine rhodamine B.200 (orange fluorescence) (Fig. 10).

Cl. novyii

Twenty-five strains of *Cl. novyii* representing all types fluoresced with an antiserum prepared against *Cl. novyii* type B. Attempts to produce type specific antisera by absorption tests have so far been unsuccessful.

These three fluorescent antisera have been used over a considerable period in epizootiological studies and have yielded most valuable information on the distribution of these organisms in nature (Batty *et al.*, 1964).

Cl. tetani

Twenty-six strains of *Cl. tetani* fell into a single group on the basis of "O" agglutination and fluorescent staining. It was suggested that this anti-serum might prove useful in the examination of material from cases of tetanus and from contaminated dressings or other materials implicated in a case.

Cl. botulinum

Fluorescent labelled antisera can also be used as a rapid method for differentiating between various types of *Cl. botulinum*. Three groups were distinguished, one group comprising types A, B and F, another group types C and D, and a single group consisting of type E only. Independent work by Boothroyd and Georgala (1964) has in the main confirmed this.

Discussion

It can be seen, provided that appropriate media are used, that many species of *Clostridium*, including extremely fastidious strains, can be grown in surface culture. The use of stiff agar results in discrete colonies in species which tend to form a spreading film on normal agar. All other methods for preventing spread are inhibitory to a greater or lesser degree. Both the use of suitable media and the inhibition of spreading are of great importance in the purification of cultures. Colonial and microscopic appearance are useful guides in identification.

Fluorescent staining techniques also make possible a precise identification of certain species of *Clostridium*. Stained slides made from the suspected lesion or other appropriate sites in animals found dying or recently dead are likely to give a picture of the relative numbers of the various clostridia present more nearly approximating to the situation at the time of death than can be obtained by culturing material taken *post mortem* and conveyed to the laboratory, often under conditions which are selective for certain organisms.

The saving in time, labour and materials resulting from the use of fluorescent staining techniques is obvious and, where applicable, the method has these very real advantages over all other methods of identification.

The authors are indebted to Dr Max Sterne for inspiration, advice and encouragement and to Mr E. A. Jones and Mr E. J. Kentish for the care with which they took the photographs.

References

BATTY, I., & WALKER, P. D. (1963*a*). The differentiation of *Clostridium septicum* and *Clostridium chauvoei* by the use of fluorescent labelled antibodies. *J. Path. Bact.*, **85**, 517.

BATTY, I., & WALKER, P. D. (1963*b*). Fluorescent labelled clostridial antisera as specific stains. *Bull. Off. int. Epiz.*, **59** (9–10), 1499–1513.

BATTY, I., & WALKER, P. D. (1964). The identification of *Clostridium novyi* (*Clostridium oedematiens*) and *Clostridium tetani* by the use of fluorescent labelled antibodies. *J. Path. Bact.*, **88**, 327.

BATTY, I., BUNTAIN, D., & WALKER, P. D. (1964). *Clostridium oedematiens*: A cause of sudden death in sheep, cattle and pigs. *Vet. Rec.*, **76**, 115.

Bergey's Manual of Determinative Bacteriology (1957). Ed. by Breed, R. S. Murray, E. G. D. & Smith, N. R. Baltimore: Williams & Wilkins Co.

BOOTHROYD, M., & GEORGALA, D. L. (1964). Immunofluorescent identification of *Clostridium botulinum*. *Nature, Lond.*, **202**, 515.

BROOKS, M. E., & EPPS, H. B. G. (1958). Taxonomic studies of the genus *Clostridium: Clostridium bifermentans* and *Clostridium sordellii*. *J. gen. Microbiol.*, **21**, 144.

BULATOVA, T. I., & KABANOVA, Y. A. (1960). Identification of the botulism pathogen with luminescent sera. *J. Microbiol.*, **31**, 403.

DOLMAN, C. E. (1957). Recent observations on type E botulism. *Canad. J. publ. Hlth*, **48**, 187.

ELLNER, P. D., & GREEN, S. S. (1963). Serological relationship between *Clostridium bifermentans* and *Clostridium sordellii* based upon soluble antigens. *J. Bact.*, **86**, 605.

FREDETTE, V. (1956). Methods for the isolation and identification of the anaerobic bacteria of medical importance. *Vermont J. med. Tech.*, **1**, 8.

GECK, P., & SZANTO, R. (1961). Examination of *Clostridium perfringens* with the fluorescent tracer technique. *Acta Microbiol. Acad. Sci. Hung.*, **8**, 423.

HELLER, C. L. (1954). A simple method for producing anaerobiosis. *J. appl. Bact.*, **17**, 202.

KALITINA, T. A. (1960). The detection of *Clostridium botulinum* by means of luminescent antibodies. Communication I: the production of specific luminescence in *Clostridium botulinum* by treatment with luminescent immune serum. *Bull. biol. med. Exp.*, **49**, 81.

McINTOSH, J., & FILDES, P. (1916). A new apparatus for the isolation and cultivation of anaerobic micro-organisms. *Lancet*, **i**, 768.

SHANK, J. L. (1963). Applications of the plastic film technique in the isolation and study of anaerobic bacteria. *J. Bact.*, **86**, 95.

SMITH, L. D. S. (1955). *Introduction to Pathogenic Anaerobes*. Chicago: University of Chicago Press.

TATAKI, H., & HUET, M. (1953). Valeur du test de l'uréase pour la différentiation de *Cl. sordellii* et *Cl. bifermentans*. *Ann. Inst. Pasteur*, **84**, 890.

WALKER, P. D., & BATTY, I. (1964). Fluorescent studies in the genus *Clostridium*. II. A rapid method for differentiating *Clostridium botulinum* types A, B and F, types C and D, and type E. *J. appl. Bact.*, **27**, 140.

WILLIS, A. T. (1960). *Anaerobic Bacteriology in Clinical Medicine*. London: Butterworth.

The Identification of Certain *Mycobacterium* Species

D. C. Cann, G. Hobbs and J. M. Shewan

Ministry of Technology, Torry Research Station, Aberdeen, Scotland

Many methods have been used for the classification and identification of members within the genus *Mycobacterium*. Such diverse features as cultural properties (Frey and Hagan, 1931; Thompson, 1932; Gordon, 1937; Gordon and Hagan, 1938; Shepard, 1957; Gordon and Mihm, 1959; Vogel, 1959), cytochemical tests (Dubos and Middlebrook, 1948; Wayne, 1959), antigenic relationships (Parlett and Youmans, 1956, 1958), pathogenicity (Kushner *et al.*, 1957, McMillen and Kushner, 1959), and sensitivity to dyes (Jones and Kubica, 1963) have all been studied. Certain of these characteristics have been subjected to Adansonian analysis (Bojalil and Cerbon, 1961; Cerbon and Bojalil, 1961; Bojalil *et al.*, 1962).

Within the groups of the rapidly growing mycobacteria and those from cold-blooded animals, the most useful tests for the identification of species are those described by Gordon and her colleagues. Many of these, however, are time-consuming, requiring up to 28 days for completion. Two additional tests giving a result within 7 days have been described by Cann and Willox (1965). The first demonstrated the lipolytic action of strains of *M. phlei* when grown on lactose egg-yolk agar (Willis and Hobbs, 1958). The second differentiated strains of *M. fortuitum* from other species by their ability to produce an intense fuchsia-coloured growth on a medium containing neutral red dye. This property is particularly useful in distinguishing between strains of *M. fortuitum* and *M. smegmatis* when both give a positive colour change on MacConkey agar.

Although pigment production, along with rate of growth and colony appearance, has been shown to be a very variable property, the production of a black, soluble, melanoid pigment by strains of *M. salmonophilum* has a definite diagnostic value. Similar pigment production by certain old cultures of *M. fortuitum* on glycerol agar was observed by Gordon and Mihm (1959), but was not investigated further except to make sure that it was not caused by a contaminant. Those strains which produce this pigment also differ from typical strains of *M. fortuitum* in their inability to grow at 37° and in the esterase pattern given after starch gel electrophoresis of enzyme

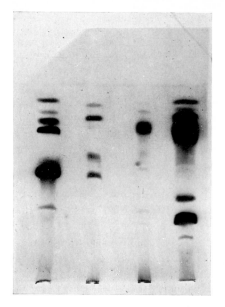

FIGS. 1–6. Enzyme patterns of rapidly growing mycobacteria after electrophoresis of ultrasonic disintegrates in starch gel, followed by staining. The direction of migration is towards the top of the photographs.

FIG. 1. The esterase patterns of four species of rapidly growing mycobacteria. From left to right: *M. phlei*, *M. rhodochrous*, *M. fortuitum* and *M. smegmatis*.

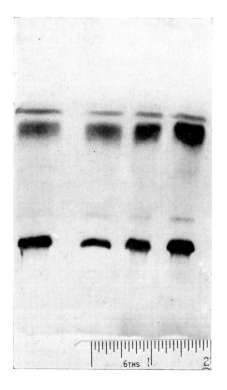

FIG. 2. Comparison of esterase patterns after growth of *M. smegmatis* (ATCC 110) at different temperatures. From left to right 30°, 37°, 40°, 45°.

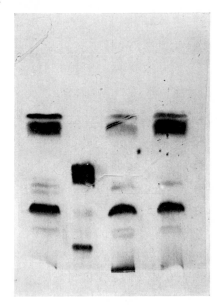

FIG. 3. Comparison of esterase patterns after growth of *M. smegmatis* on three different culture media. From left to right: lemco agar, horse plasma marker, blood agar, glycerol agar.

FIG. 4. Effect of age of culture on esterase patterns of *M. smegmatis*. From left to right: horse plasma marker, 3, 7 and 14 days' incubation.

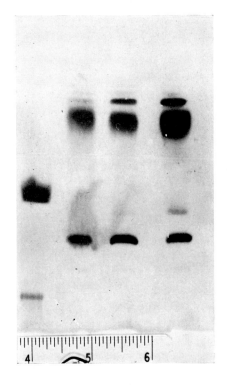

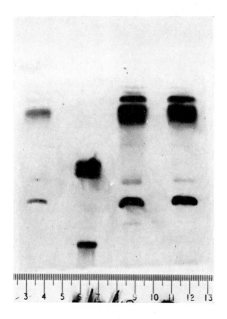

FIG. 5.   Comparison of three methods of preparing enzyme extracts. From left to right: freezing and thawing; horse plasma marker; shaking in a Mickle disintegrator; ultrasonic disintegration.

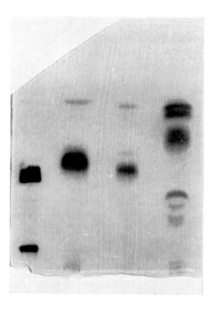

FIG. 6. Esterase patterns of three strains of mycobacteria classified, by means of physiological tests, as *M. fortuitum*. A horse plasma marker was included in the gel. From left to right: horse plasma marker; strain M33; strain NCTC 2006 and strain NCTC 946.

preparations. Further differences in the reactions of these cultures may well lead to a subdivision of the species, *M. fortuitum*, if not the creation of a new species.

The technique of esterase analysis has been profitably used for the identification of *Bacillus thuringiensis* (Norris and Burges, 1963; Norris, 1964), certain mycobacteria (Cann and Willox, 1965) and *Vibrio* spp. (Willox and Shewan, 1963). The type of pattern given by members of the rapidly growing mycobacteria and those from cold-blooded animals is distinct for each species (Fig. 1). The use of such a technique, however, depends on reproducibility, and it has been shown that such patterns are stable over a range of cultural conditions (Figs. 2–4) and with efficient methods of enzyme preparation (Fig. 5). The advantages of esterase analysis, when compared with the usual biochemical and physiological tests, are the economy in time and materials, coupled with equal reliability and greater sensitivity in detecting differences between strains. This is demonstrated in Fig. 6, where three cultures, classified as *M. fortuitum* (Gordon and Mihm, 1959), are seen to be dissimilar. The culture M33 was considered to be a new species, *M. salmonophilum*, when isolated (Ross, 1960). Although it is doubtful that this is so, as many of its properties, including the esterase pattern, are similar to strain NCTC 2006, isolated as long ago as 1925, it is obviously different from a typical culture of *M. fortuitum* (NCTC 946).

The work described in this paper was carried out as part of the programme of the Department of Scientific and Industrial Research.

References

BOJALIL, L. F., & CERBON, J. (1961). Taxonomic analysis of nonpigmented, rapidly growing mycobacteria. *J. Bact.*, **81**, 338.

BOJALIL, L. F., CERBON, J., & TRUJILLO, A. (1962). Adansonian classification of mycobacteria. *J. gen. Microbiol.*, **28**, 333.

CANN, D. C., & WILLOX, M. E. (1965). Analysis of multimolecular enzymes as an aid to the identification of certain rapidly growing mycobacteria, using starch gel electrophoresis. *J. appl. Bact.*, **28**, 165.

CERBON, J., & BOJALIL, L. F. (1961). Physiological relationships of rapidly growing mycobacteria. *J. gen. Microbiol.*, **25**, 7.

DUBOS, R. J., & MIDDLEBROOK, G. (1948). Cytochemical reactions of virulent tubercle bacilli. *Am. Rev. Tuberc. pulm. Dis.*, **58**, 698.

FREY, C. A., & HAGAN, W. A. (1931). The distribution of acid-fast bacteria in soils. *J. infect. Dis.*, **49**, 497.

GORDON, R. E. (1937). The classification of acid-fast bacteria, I. *J. Bact.*, **34**, 617.

GORDON, R. E., & HAGAN, W. A. (1938). The classification of acid-fast bacteria, II. *J. Bact.*, **36**, 39.

GORDON, R. E., & MIHM, J. M. (1959). A comparison of four species of mycobacteria. *J. gen. Microbiol.*, **21**, 736.

JONES, W. D., & KUBICA, G. P. (1963). The differential typing of certain rapidly growing mycobacteria based on their sensitivity to certain dyes. *Am. Rev. resp. Dis.*, **88,** 335.

KUSHNER, D. S., MCMILLEN, S., & SENDERI, M. (1957). Atypical acid-fast bacilli, II. *Mycobacterium fortuitum.* Bacteriologic characteristics and pathogenicity for laboratory animals. *Am. Rev. Tuberc. pulm. Dis.*, **76,** 108.

MCMILLEN, S., & KUSHNER, D. S. (1959). Atypical acid-fast bacilli, III. An expanded schema. *Am. Rev. resp. Dis.*, **80,** 434.

NORRIS, J. R. (1964). The classification of *Bacillus thuringiensis. J. appl. Bact.*, **27,** 439.

NORRIS, J. R., & BURGES, H. D. (1963). Esterases of crystalliferous bacteria pathogenic for insects; epizootiological applications. *J. Insect Path.*, **5,** 460.

PARLETT, R. G., & YOUMANS, G. P. (1956). Antigenic relationships between mycobacteria as determined by agar diffusion precipitin techniques. *Am. Rev. Tuberc. pulm. Dis.*, **73,** 637.

PARLETT, R. G., & YOUMANS, G. P. (1958). Antigenic relationships between ninety-eight strains of mycobacteria using gel diffusion precipitation techniques. *Am. Rev. Tuberc. pulm. Dis.*, **77,** 450.

ROSS, A. J. (1960). *Mycobacterium salmonophilum* sp. nov. from salmonoid fishes. *Am. Rev. resp. Dis.*, **81** (2), 241.

SHEPARD, C. C. (1957). Growth characteristics in Hela cells of the rapidly growing acid-fast bacteria, *Mycobacterium fortuitum, Mycobacterium phlei,* and *Mycobacterium smegmatis. J. Bact.*, **73,** 722.

THOMPSON, H. M. (1932). Studies on saphrophytic acid-fast bacteria. *Am. Rev. Tuberc. pulm. Dis.*, **26,** 162.

VOGEL, H. (1959). A metabolic study of acid-fast bacteria from cold blooded animals. *J. infect. Dis.*, **104,** 28.

WAYNE, L. G. (1959). Quantitative aspects of neutral red reactions of typical and atypical mycobacteria. *Am. Rev. Tuberc. pulm. Dis.*, **79,** 526.

WILLIS, A. T., & HOBBS, G. (1958). A medium for the identification of clostridia producing opalescence in egg-yolk emulsions. *J. Path. Bact.*, **75,** 299.

WILLOX, M. E., & SHEWAN, J. M. (1963). Annual Report. Torry Research Station, Aberdeen, Scotland.

An Alternative Approach to the Identification of *Streptomyces* Species: a Working System

T. Cross and A. M. MacIver

Department of Biological Sciences, Bradford Institute of Technology, Bradford 7, Yorkshire, England

Streptomyces species are very common in soil; they are also found frequently on vegetable and animal materials, as a constituent of the air flora, in fresh-water supplies and in marine environments. They are responsible for the decomposition and degradation of a wide range of natural and synthetic organic compounds. However, they are invariably either referred to in papers as *Streptomyces* spp. below a list of named fungi and bacteria whenever a mixed microflora is examined or else completely neglected. This is due in part to the lack of specialists in this particular group, but it is also a reflection of the chaotic state of actinomycete taxonomy. Attempts are being made to remedy this situation, but it could be some years before a workable system is available.

There are a number of keys of varying usefulness available, but the majority are very misleading to microbiologists who have not spent several years working with the genus. The keys of Waksman (1959, 1961) are difficult to comprehend, as are those in Bergey's Manual of Determinative Bacteriology (Breed *et al.*, 1948; Breed *et al.*, 1957). The English and German translations of Krasil'nikov's book (1941) are of some value, but the descriptions of species given are very often incomplete and the nomenclature differs radically from that currently accepted in the West. One can use the useful guide compiled by Pridham *et al.* (1958), thus reducing the number of possibilities, but one could be left with a score or more of alternative specific names and the final choice can be extremely difficult, as discovered by groups of experienced investigators engaged on co-operative studies (Küster, 1960; Gottlieb, 1961). By using the key of Ettlinger *et al.* (1958) a specific name could be applied to a number of isolates, but the number of species included in this classification is limited.

Microbiologists require a system that will enable them to label each *Streptomyces* isolate with a name or code which could be related to specific names as they become accepted. We give below a possible scheme for consideration and discussion.

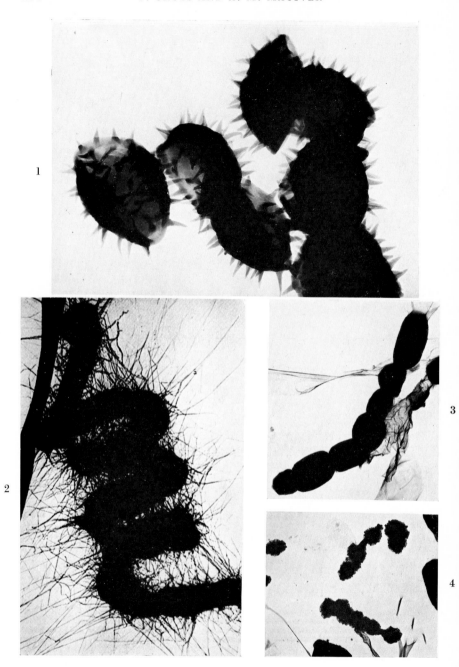

FIGS. 1–4. Surface morphology of spores. (1) Spines; (2) Hairs; (3) Smooth; (4) Warts.

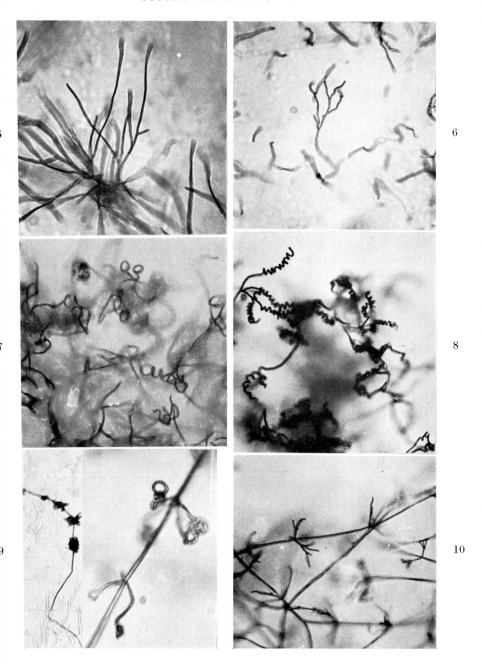

FIGS. 5–10. Aerial mycelium morphology. (5) Rectus; (6) Flexibilis; (7) Retinaculum Apertum; (8) Spira; (9) Monoverticillus Spira; (10) Biverticillus.

This scheme makes use of a number of characteristics which are currently regarded as useful in the identification of species. These characteristics are coded and the specific name is replaced by a series of letters and numbers which serve also to describe the properties of the culture. A similar scheme was suggested previously by Flaig and Kutzner (1958), but a greater number of characteristics were included, some of which are now regarded as being of doubtful utility.

Characteristics

(1) *Production of a melanin pigment.* Two media are used for pigment production:
    (*a*) peptone-iron agar + yeast extract (Tresner and Danga, 1958) and
    (*b*) tryptone-casein-nitrate medium (Menzies and Dade, 1959).
See also Küster (1960, 1963), Küster and Williams (1964), Prauser and Meyer (1961) and Turri and Silvestri (1960).

(2) *Surface morphology of spores.* This is determined with the electron microscope (Küster, 1953; Tresner *et al.*, 1961). Spores are smooth, spiny, hairy or warty (Figs. 1–4).

(3) *Aerial mycelium morphology.* The morphology of the aerial mycelium is used to divide the genus into the groups:
    Rectus—straight,
    Flexibilis—flexuous,
    Retinaculum Apertum—open loops, hooks or extended spirals of wide diameter,
    Spira—simple spirals, not on verticils; spirals may be short and compact or long extended or open,
    Monoverticillus—primary whorls distributed on a long axis or branch; no spirals,
    Monoverticillus spira—primary verticils or whorls distributed on a long axis; elements of verticils spiralled,
    Biverticillus—compound verticils or whorls on a long axis; no spirals,
    Biverticillus spira—compound verticils, elements of secondary verticils spiralled (Figs. 5–10).
See also Pridham *et al.* (1958); Ettlinger *et al.* (1958).

(4) *Colour of the aerial mycelium.* The colours of the mycelium are described as follows:
    1. *niveus*—snow white.
    2. *griseus*—yellowish to greenish grey.
    3. *azureus*—sky blue.
    4. *cinnamoneus*—pale carmine darkening through admixtures of grey to cinnamon brown.

5. *cinereus*—ash grey with an admixture of cinnamon brown, sky blue, greenish yellow or olive green.

6. *prasinus*—leek green.

See Ettlinger *et al.* (1958).

(5) *Substrate mycelium colour.* Substrate mycelium colours are described as:

1. *buff*—colourless—cream grey—brown. Includes all shades of brown to black with admixtures (tints) of other colours—yellow, blue, red and green.

2. *buff* + *yellow*—significant yellow component to give gold, citron, yellow orange, etc.

3. *buff* + *red.*

4. *buff* + *blue*—includes the blue violet and blue red pigments with indicator properties.

5. *buff* + *green.*

(This is a slight modification of the Szabo and Marton (1962) scheme.)

(6) *Carbon compound utilization.* A limited number of carbon sources can be included to give further differentiation.

The substrates suggested are:

1. L-arabinose.
2. D-fructose.
3. I-inositol.
4. D-mannitol.
5. Raffinose.
6. L-rhamnose.
7. Sucrose.
8. D-xylose.

See Zahner and Ettlinger (1957), Pridham and Gottlieb (1948), Benedict *et al.* (1955).

The above properties have been coidfied in the Key given in Table 1.

Example

A particular isolate, after observing the growth and morphology, etc., on a number of media would be referred to as:

Streptomyces M2, S1, A4, C1, G1 (U2, 4, 8)

        i.e. melanin negative

           smooth spores

           spiral spore chains

           white aerial mycelium

           buff (yellow-brown) substrate mycelium

           able to utilize fructose, mannitol, xylose.

In this case it would be a relatively simple task to give an accepted specific name, *S. albus*, to this organism as it has been fully described (Lyons and

TABLE 1. Key to description of streptomyces

Character	Code
(1) Melanin positive	M1
negative	M2
(2) Spore surface smooth	S1
spines	S2
hairs	S3
warts	S4
(3) Aerial mycelium morphology	
Rectus	A1
Flexibilis	A2
Retinaculum Apertum	A3
Spira	A4
Monoverticillus	A5
Monoverticillus Spira	A6
Biverticillus	A7
Biverticillus Spira	A8
(4) Colour of aerial mycelium	
niveus	C1
griseus	C2
azureus	C3
cinnamoneus	C4
cinereus	C5
prasinus	C6
(5) Substrate mycelium colour	
buff	G1
buff + yellow	G2
buff + red	G3
buff + blue	G4
buff + green	G5
(6) Carbon utilization	
arabinose	U1
fructose	U2
inositol	U3
mannitol	U4
raffinose	U5
rhamnose	U6
sucrose	U7
xylose	U8

Pridham, 1962). There are, however, a number of permutations of these code numbers which would describe an organism adequately for comparative work by other investigators, but would mean extensive observation, comparisons and literature surveys to discover a suitable Linnean binomial.

In suggesting this scheme we are not proposing to ignore or displace current schemes for the taxonomy of the *Streptomyces*. It is purely an attempt to provide a working system for use at the present time until an adequate scheme is available and to encourage microbiologists to consider the streptomycetes in their work. We have been asked if this scheme could be incorporated into a conventional taxonomic system. The thought of reducing the rank of so many described species is almost impossible to contemplate, but one way would be to reduce the genus *Streptomyces* to two species: *S. chromogenes* (A. Chromogenus Gasperini), melanin positive; and *S. albus* (Rossi Doria) Waksman et Henrici, melanin negative. Each species would have a number of strains distinguished by code letters and numbers.

References

BENEDICT, R. G., PRIDHAM, T. G., LINDENFELSER, A., HALL, H. H., & JACKSON, R. W. (1955). Further studies in the evaluation of carbohydrate utilization tests as aids in the differentiation of species of Streptomyces. *Appl. Microbiol.*, **3**, 1.

BREED, R. S., MURRAY, E. G. D., & HITCHENS, A. P. (1948). *Bergey's manual of determinative bacteriology, 6th ed.* London: Baillière, Tindall & Cox.

BREED, R. S., MURRAY, E. G. D., & SMITH, N. R. (1957). *Bergey's manual of determinative bacteriology. 7th ed.* London: Baillière, Tindall & Cox, Ltd.

ETTLINGER, L., CORBAZ, R., & HUTTER, R. (1958). Zur Systematik der Actinomyceten, 4. Eine Arteinteilung der Gattung Streptomyces Waksman et Henrici. *Arch. Mikrobiol.*, **31**, 326.

FLAIG, W., & KUTZNER, H. J. (1958). *Beitrag zur Systematik und Okologie der Gattung Streptomyces* Waksman et Henrici. Braunschweig Volkenrode, Braunschweig.

GOTTLIEB, D. (1961). An evaluation of criteria and procedures used in the description and characterization of the Streptomycetes. *Appl. Microbiol.*, **9**, 55.

KRASIL'NIKOV, N. A. (1941). *Actinomycetales.* Moscow Acad. Sci., U.S.S.R.

KÜSTER, E. (1953). Beitrag zur Genese und Morphologie der Streptomyceten Sporen. *6th Internat. Congr. Microbiol. Rome 1953*, **1**, 114.

KÜSTER, E. (1960). Results of a comparative study of criteria used in the classification of the Actinomycetales. *Int. Bull. bact. Nomencl. Taxon.*, **11**, 91.

KÜSTER, E. (1963). Morphological and physiological aspects of the taxonomy of Streptomycetes. *Microbiología esp.*, **16**, 193.

KÜSTER, E., & WILLIAMS, S. T. (1964). Production of hydrogen sulphide by Streptomycetes and methods for its detection. *Appl. Microbiol.*, **12**, 46.

LYONS, A. J., & PRIDHAM, T. G. (1962). Proposal to designate strain ATCC 3004 (IMRU 3004) as the neotype strain of *Streptomyces albus* (Rossi-Doria) Waksman et Henrici. *J. Bact.*, **83**, 370.

MENZIES, J. D., & DADE, C. E. (1959). A selective indicator medium for isolating *S. scabies* from potato tubers or soil. *Phytopathology*, **49**, 457.

PRAUSER, H., & MEYER, J. (1961). Zum Nachweis der H_2S Bildung bei Streptomyceten. *Naturwis.*, **48**, 463.

PRIDHAM, T. G., & GOTTLIEB, D. (1948). The utilization of carbon compounds by some Actinomycetales as an aid for species determination. *J. Bact.*, **56**, 107.

PRIDHAM, T. G., HESSELTINE, C. W., & BENEDICT, R. G. (1958). A guide for the classification of Streptomycetes according to selected groups. *Appl. Microbiol.*, **6**, 52.

SZABO, I., & MARTON, M. (1962). Beitrag zur Systematik der nicht verticillaten *Streptomyces* Arten. *Zbl. Bakt. Abt. II.*, **115**, 380.

TRESNER, H. D., & DANGA, F. (1958). Hydrogen sulphide production of *Streptomyces* as a criterion for species differentiation. *J. Bact.*, **76**, 239.

TRESNER, H. D., DAVIES, M. C., & BACKUS, E. J. (1961). Electron microscopy of Streptomyces spore morphology and its role in species differentiation. *J. Bact.*, **81**, 70.

TURRI, M., & SILVESTRI, L. (1960). Osservazioni su un saggio biochemico proposto per la classificazione degli Attinomiceti. *Annali Microbiol.*, **10**, 71.

WAKSMAN, S. A. (1959, 1961). *The Actinomycetes. Vol. I. Nature, Occurrence and Activities; Vol. II Classification, Identification and Descriptions of Genera and Species.* Baltimore: Williams & Wilkins.

ZAHNER, H., & ETTLINGER, L. (1957). Zur Systematik der Actinomyceten. 3. Die Verwertung verschiedener Kohlenstoffquellen als Hilfsmittel der Artbestimmung innerhalb der Gattung Streptomyces. *Arch. Microbiol.*, **26**, 307.

Rapid and Simple Biochemical Tests for Bacterial Identification

Patricia H. Clarke

Biochemistry Department, University College, London, England

AND THE LATE K. J. Steel

Central Public Health Laboratory, Colindale, London, England

The traditional range of biochemical tests has developed by a process of accretion. A reaction has been found useful in characterizing certain species and has then been applied to others so that the total number of tests available has steadily increased. In the classical type of test, using cultures growing in complicated media, the final result is often due to a series of enzymes acting on a number of substrates; thus a positive result in any test is no guarantee that two different organisms contain the same enzyme. This is the case in such ill-defined tests as sugar fermentation, when the pathways of hexose catabolism may be different, and the product giving rise to the colour change of the indicator may be any of a number of organic acids. Equally, negative results in such tests may be caused by many enzyme differences. Some tests with growing cultures depend on single enzyme reactions with defined substrates, e.g. urease and catalase tests, but these are so arranged that each culture is tested for only one enzyme at a time and the culture is grown for a day or more in liquid or solid media.

We have been exploring techniques for testing cultures for the presence or absence of single enzymes using pure substrates. The criteria we had in mind were the following: (1) each culture was to be tested for several enzymes simultaneously, (2) the tests were to be completed within a few hours, and (3) the procedure was to be simple enough to apply to a large number of cultures.

For the methods which were finally adopted the bacteria were grown overnight as a lawn culture on nutrient agar. The test substrate was applied in the form of a paper disc impregnated with a suitable concentration of the substrate compound, and the cultures incubated for one to four hours before examination. The simplest of the tests were those using chromogenic substrates, when as the result of enzyme action coloured products were released. This has only limited application, since chromogenic substrates are not available for most enzymes. A more general method is to add a reagent which reacts with the enzyme product to form a coloured compound. This method was used for a number of tests and the reagent was usually applied with a dropping pipette, but chemically stable reagents could also be applied as impregnated paper discs which could be placed over the substrate discs after the incubation period for enzyme action. Another possible method is to include in the medium an indicator compound which responds by some colour change to the presence of the enzyme product, and this was used for one type of test.

One problem which must be considered in tests of this sort is the effect of the growth medium on the enzymes produced by the culture. For the tests described below we used a nutrient agar which allowed good growth of the strains used. In some cases it might be an advantage to devise media which encouraged the synthesis of the enzymes to be tested. For one induced enzyme in our series of tests we first induced synthesis of β-galactosidase by adding a lactose-impregnated disc and followed this after 2 h at 37° by a disc impregnated with the chromogenic substrate o-nitrophenyl-β-D-galactoside, which is a substrate but not an inducer of the enzyme.

In this preliminary survey some tests were devised which would correspond to those commonly used by bacteriologists. The paper-disc tests for acetoin, indole production and amino-acid oxidase were carried out on standard cultures and the results agreed well with those obtained by conventional methods.

No general claims are being made for the particular merits of tests included here; they are examples of enzyme reactions which could be studied by this technique. The method is very simple and it would not be difficult to devise tests for a number of different bacterial enzymes, e.g. nitrate reductase, proteolytic enzymes, sulphatases and phosphatases.

In working out the detailed conditions for any test it is important to ensure that no significant reactions are given by (a) the paper used to prepare the discs, or (b) the medium used to grow the culture. When the test is one related to a standard bacteriological test, known positive and negative cultures should be thoroughly tested over a range of test conditions.

Methods

Cultures. The cultures were grown on the surface of agar plates by spreading 0·2 ml of a broth culture over the agar surface but poured plates can be used if preferred.

Preparation of paper discs. Various grades of filter paper were tested and although all were reasonably satisfactory, Whatman 3 MM was preferred, chiefly for its high absorption capacity. Two methods were used to apply the compounds to the paper. For method 1, which was particularly suitable for low concentrations, a standard solution of the compound was prepared and 5–25 μl was applied with a micropipette, drying between additions. For method 2 the papers were soaked in a solution of appropriate strength. The papers were dried either at room temperature or in an incubator at 37°. In the earlier experiments discs of different shapes were used to identify the various substrates, but later the discs were all made of uniform size, 1 cm², and identified by a typewritten code. It was found convenient to cut the paper into discs after impregnation with the various compounds. The paper discs were all stored in screw-cap bottles at room temperature. Examples of systems to which the method has been applied are detailed below.

Esterase activity

Substrate; indoxyl acetate (0·05 mg/disc applied from alcoholic solution).
Organism to demonstrate test; *Bacillus cereus.*

This is an example of a test using a chromogenic substrate. Esterases are widespread among bacteria, and indoxyl acetate is rapidly hydrolysed by certain esterases. The hydrolysis product is rapidly oxidized in air to indican, which has a deep blue colour. With strongly positive cultures the colour reaction develops within a few minutes. Roughly quantitative values can be obtained by noting the times taken to produce the colour reaction. Other chromogenic ester substrates are available, e.g. indoxyl butyrate, β-naphthyl acetate.

β-galactosidase activity

Inducer; lactose (15 mg/disc).
Substrate; o-nitrophenyl-β-D-galactoside (0·1 mg/disc).
Organism to demonstrate test; *Escherichia coli.*

The inducer disc is applied to the plate culture, which is then incubated at 37° for 2 h to induce β-galactosidase synthesis. The substrate disc is then applied overlapping the lactose disc.

Lactose induces the synthesis of β-galactosidase, the first of the sequence of enzymes required for the fermentation or oxidation of lactose. The enzyme also hydrolyses the chromogenic substrate o-nitrophenyl-β-D-galactoside, producing o-nitrophenol, which is yellow in colour. This is a sensitive reaction and with positive cultures the colour reaction develops after about 15 min.

Tryptophanase activity

Substrate: tryptophan (disc soaked in 1% aqueous solution).
Organism to demonstrate test: *Escherichia coli*.

Tryptophan is cleaved by tryptophanase to ammonia, pyruvate and indole. After incubation at 37° for 2 h the test for indole is carried out by adding 1 drop of Kovacs reagent (5% p-dimethylaminobenzaldehyde in 75 ml iso-amyl alcohol + 25 ml conc. HCl). With positive cultures the red-coloured complex is formed almost immediately after adding the reagent. The colour is not stable and fades after about 15 min.

Aminoacid oxidase activity

Substrate: DL phenylalanine (discs soaked in 1% aqueous solution).
Organism to demonstrate test: *Proteus* sp.

This enzyme oxidatively deaminates a number of L-aminoacids to form the corresponding ketoacids. After incubation at 37° for 2 h the test for phenylpyruvic acid is carried out by adding one drop of ferric chloride solution (10% in dil. HCl). A deep green-blue develops in about 1 min with positive cultures. This gradually changes to a darker colour, but does not fade. Most α-ketoacids give coloured complexes with ferric ions and this test can be adapted to use other aminoacids as substrates.

Acetoin production (Vosges-Proskauer test)

Substrate: sodium pyruvate (disc soaked in 10% solution).
Organism to demonstrate test: *Aeromonas hydrophila*.

Acetoin (acetylmethylcarbinol $CH_3COCHOHCH_3$) is recognized as a possible end-product of sugar fermentation. Pyruvate formed from hexose breakdown is first condensed to form α-acetolactate, which is then de-carboxylated to acetoin. α-acetolactate decarboxylase is induced by growth at an acid pH. For this test we grew the culture on 1% glucose agar. After incubation with the substrate disc for 2 h at 37° the test for acetoin was carried out by adding 1 drop 40% KOH, 1 drop 1% creatine and 1 drop 1% α-naphthol in alcohol. The test reagents convert acetoin to diacetyl, which reacts with creatine in the presence of α-naphthol to form the deep red complex. Several variations of the test reagents are in use and probably any of these could be used instead.

Acid production from sugars, etc.

Substrates: glucose, lactose, sucrose, maltose and mannitol (15 mg/disc).

The indicator is incorporated in the nutrient agar; both phenol red and bromcresol purple give promising results. The method is essentially that described by Sanders *et al.* (1957).

Although acid production from sugars is due to a series of enzymes it was included in this series because such tests are widely used by bacteriologists and a paper-disc method had already been suggested. In our tests 4 h appeared to be a suitable incubation period.

Reference

SANDERS, A. C., FABER, J. E., & COOK, T. M. (1957). A rapid method for the characterization of enteric pathogen using paper discs. *Appl. Microbiol.*, **5,** 36.

A Multi-point Inoculation Method
for Performing Biochemical Tests on Bacteria

M. GOODFELLOW AND T. R. G. GRAY

Hartley Botanical Laboratories, The University, Liverpool, England

The importance of rapid testing procedures for examining the biochemical properties of bacteria has long been recognized. Recently Sneath (1962) suggested that multi-point inoculation methods coupled with the internal division of Petri dishes into separate compartments containing test substrates would prove useful in this respect. Harris (1963) described a method of a similar type which involved the simultaneous inoculation of small agar-medium discs positioned on the base of a Petri dish. No attempt was made to separate the agar discs with internal barriers in the dish. In view of the well-known spreading ability of many bacteria and their ready passage through water films, a number of limitations to this technique become apparent. Another method described by Quadling and Colwell (1964) overcame this problem: their method involved the use of a multi-point inoculator which introduced bacteria into separate test tubes. The main drawbacks to this method are the complexity of the apparatus and the storage problems created by the inoculation of a large number of test tubes.

To alleviate some of these problems, we have devised multi-point inoculation methods (Gray and Goodfellow, 1966) involving the actual internal division of Petri dishes into separate compartments. One of these methods is described here, together with its applications and limitations.

Apparatus

An aluminium plate drilled with twenty-five holes (9mm diam) and supported on short legs (*c.* 6 mm high) is placed in a Petri dish. In the holes are fitted small flat-bottomed glass vials (9 × 10 mm) (Astell Ltd, London) (Fig. 1). The vials may be filled with either sterile solid or liquid test media.

To inoculate these vials with bacteria, the multi-point inoculator described by Tarr (1958) is used (J. Biddulph and Co. Ltd, Manchester) (Fig. 2). Twenty-five different cultures or suspensions of bacteria to be examined are placed in empty sterile vials in a master plate which is placed on the inoculator platform. The plate is lifted by raising the inoculator platform until the wire loops dip into the cultures. The master plate is then removed and replaced by a plate containing twenty-five vials of a test medium, which are then inoculated by raising the inoculator platform. The procedure is repeated for other plates containing different test media. If

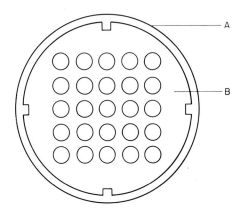

FIG. 1. (*a*) Side elevation of a divided Petri dish showing five vials in place.
A. Petri dish; B. Aluminium plate; C. Glass vials full of medium.
(*b*) Surface view of an aluminium plate inside a Petri dish.
A. Petri dish; B. Aluminium plate, drilled with twenty-five holes.

necessary the loops are sterilized and recharged between each batch of inoculations. The inoculated plates are then incubated for appropriate periods of time.

Cross-contamination between vials

To test the possibility of cross-contamination between vials containing different types of bacteria, strains of *Proteus vulgaris*, *Proteus mirabilis* and *Bacillus cereus mycoides* were inoculated into some compartments of plates containing starch agar (Conn, Jennison and Weeks, 1957). Other compartments were left uninoculated. A control plate containing starch agar but with no division into compartments was also inoculated. The plates were incubated at 37° and 25° and examined after 1, 2 and 7 days. After 2 days, growth in the control cultures had spread over considerable areas of the plates, but, even after 7 days, growth in the separate vials was always restricted to those that had been inoculated.

FIG. 2. Multi-point inoculator (Tarr, 1958), with a dish containing bacterial cultures on the inoculator platform.

Restriction of bacterial metabolites and enzymes to individual compartments

The restriction of bacterial metabolites and enzymes to inoculated compartments was demonstrated by inoculating *Proteus vulgaris* into vials containing potassium nitrate agar (Conn *et al.*, 1957). After incubation for 1 week, Griess-Ilosvay's reagents I and II (Wilson and Miles, 1955) were added to the culture medium and the presence or absence of nitrite determined. The red coloration indicating presence of nitrite developed only in the inoculated vials (Fig. 3).

A similar test was performed to demonstrate the production of acid from glucose by a series of cultures including *Escherichia coli*, using the medium of Hugh and Leifson (1953). After 1 or 2 days' incubation acid production had occurred: again, the reaction was associated only with inoculated vials. However, after longer incubation periods acidity sometimes developed in uninoculated vials. These vials were still sterile, so presumably they had absorbed volatile acids in sufficient quantity to change the pH. Fortunately, acidity developed in inoculated vials much more rapidly than in the larger amounts of medium used in corresponding test-tube cultures, so it was possible to read the results before they became obscured. In some inoculated vials acidity was observed after only 6 h of incubation.

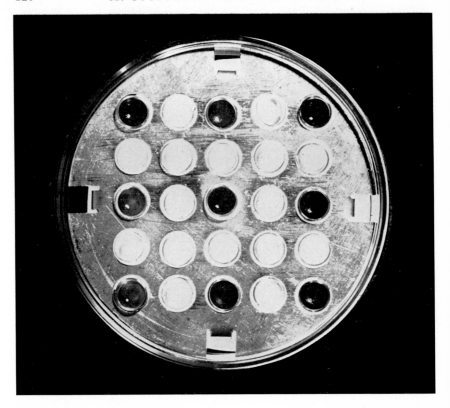

FIG. 3. A plate containing potassium nitrate agar inoculated with *Proteus vulgaris*, incubated for 7 days at 37° and treated with Griess-Ilosvay's reagents. Note the colour which has developed in the inoculated vials only.

The production and detection of gaseous metabolites

The detection of gas produced from sugars by cultures growing on the surface of solid media was achieved by covering the agar with a glass or plastic square or disc. Gas bubbles collected beneath the surface of the glass. The production of hydrogen sulphide from sulphur compounds was detected in a similar way. *Escherichia coli* was inoculated on to Difco peptone iron agar: part of the culture was covered with a glass square and part left uncovered: blackening of the medium occurred only where the culture was covered (Fig. 4). When the square was removed the black coloration disappeared within 6 h. Parallel experiments were performed in an anaerobic jar. Under these conditions blackening of the medium still did not occur unless the culture was covered. However, when the disc was removed and the plate replaced under anaerobic conditions, the black colour persisted.

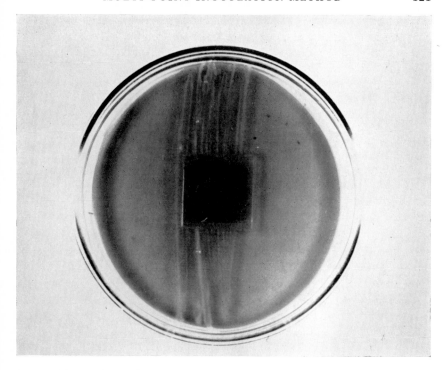

FIG. 4. Plate culture showing the production of hydrogen sulphide. Note the intense blackening of the medium under the coverslip.

It was considered, therefore, that both the prevention of diffusion of hydrogen sulphide into the atmosphere *and* the maintenance of ferrous sulphides in a reduced state were of importance in producing a positive result. This supplements and confirms the interpretation of Küster and Williams (1964) on the use of surface inoculation of peptone iron agar for detecting hydrogen sulphide production. Experiments involving the use of discs within the small vials are now in progress.

The use of liquid test media

Tests for the utilization of single carbon and nitrogen sources and growth factors are better performed in liquid media, since agar may contain other contaminating substances. Assessment of growth in liquid media was made by determining the development of turbidity in media containing different nutrients. Only moderately heavy growth could be detected because of the small quantities of media contained in the vials. Consequently these tests

may not be as sensitive as those carried out in test tubes. Between inoculations, loops should be thoroughly washed to minimize the carry-over of
nutrients from one medium to another, and then flamed; preferably, loops
should be replaced with needles. The incorporation of nutrients in an inert
silica gel may make these tests easier to perform and interpret. The more
readily and quickly prepared silica gel recently described by Funk and
Krulwich (1964) might be very useful for this purpose.

Range of possible tests

In addition to those tests already described, those involving breakdown of
polysaccharides, e.g. starch or chitin, can be performed using this method,
assessing the results by the reaction of the medium to iodine or by the
clearing of opacity respectively. Sensitivity to antibiotics and other inhibitors, production of oxidase and catalase, release of ammonia from urea
and the hydrolysis of aesculin, tributyrin and gelatin may also be determined. Other tests should prove equally adaptable.

Advantages of the method

The method described is not essentially different from other similar techniques. However, it combines the simultaneous inoculation of cultures with
the division of Petri dishes into quite distinct compartments. Because of the
size of the compartments only small volumes of media are required, and
since these are inoculated with comparatively large numbers of bacterial
cells, the results of the tests are often known in a few hours. Presumably
the sensitivity of such tests will differ from those normally carried out in
test tubes; this may limit the value of the technique for identifying bacteria
until the reactions of known strains have been determined. However, its
value for gathering taxonomic information, particularly for subsequent use
in Adansonian analyses is not impaired, since it is still possible to record a
series of yes/no answers for a number of tests under standard conditions.

References

CONN, H. J., JENNISON, M. W., & WEEKS, O. B. (1957). Routine tests for
   the identification of bacteria. In *Manual of Microbiological Methods*, edited for
   the Society of American Bacteriologists by Pelczar, M. J., *et al.* New York:
   McGraw Hill Book Co. Inc.
FUNK, H. B., & KRULWICH, T. A. (1964). Preparation of clear silica gels that
   can be streaked. *J. Bact.*, **88**, 1200.
GRAY, T. R. G., & GOODFELLOW, M. (1966). Rapid methods of making

routine physiological tests on soil bacteria. *Proc. VIIIth Int. Congr. Soil Sci.*, *Bucharest, Commission III* (in the press).

HARRIS, P. J. (1963). A replica plating culture technique. *J. appl. Bact.*, **26**, 100.

HUGH, R., & LEIFSON, E. (1953). The taxonomic significance of fermentative versus oxidative metabolism of carbohydrates by various Gram-negative bacteria. *J. Bact.*, **66**, 24.

KÜSTER, E., & WILLIAMS, S. T. (1964). Production of hydrogen sulphide by streptomycetes and methods for its detection. *Appl. Microbiol.*, **12**, 46.

QUADLING, C., & COLWELL, R. R. (1964). Apparatus for simultaneous inoculation of culture tubes. *Can. J. Microbiol.*, **10**, 87.

SNEATH, P. H. A. (1962). The construction of taxonomic groups. In *Microbial Classification*, edited by Ainsworth, G. C., and Sneath, P. H. A. *Symp. Soc. Gen. Microbiol.*, No. 12, 288.

TARR, H. A. (1958). Mechanical aids for the phage-typing of *Staphylococcus aureus. Mon. Bull. Minist. Hlth Lab. Serv.*, **17**, 64.

WILSON, G. S., & MILES, A. A. (1955). *Topley and Wilson's Principles of Bacteriology and Immunity*, 4th ed., p. 451. London: Arnold.

An Automatic Multi-point Inoculator for Petri Dishes

P. Ridgway Watt, L. Jeffries and S. A. Price

*Vitamins Limited, Walton Oaks Experimental Station,
Tadworth, Surrey, England*

Multiple surface inoculation of culture media in Petri dishes with cultures of fungi, yeasts, bacteria, bacteriophages or indicator organisms for determination of colicine production is practised in many laboratories. This procedure, when carried out sequentially by hand, is tedious and time consuming. There is, furthermore, a risk of airborne contamination.

To facilitate such inoculations several investigators have proposed manually operated mechanical devices for the simultaneous transference of the required number of inocula to the agar surface and at least one such unit is commercially available. Thus, Beech, Carr and Codner (1955) have modified for use with bacteria and yeasts the device proposed by Garrett (1946). Tarr (1958) described an applicator for placing simultaneously and accurately up to twenty-five standard drops of bacteriophage on to a seeded agar surface and Lidwell (1959) has further mechanized this device for phage-typing studies. A simple multipoint device was also described by Smith (1961) for the purpose of screening cultures for lysogeny and for studying the growth responses of mutant strains.

Manually operated devices suffer from the disadvantage that there is a tendency for the volumes transferred to be influenced by individual variations in the speed of operation. Moreover, there may be a risk of cross-contamination of the inoculum cups through drops falling off the loops during transfer. The apparatus described here avoids operator variations by the use of an entirely motorized drive, and transfers up to twenty-eight inocula, under cover, at the rate of nine complete plates per minute.

Description and Operation of Apparatus

A vertical shaft at the back of the machine carries a horizontal plate through which the inoculating pins hang freely in a regular but asymmetrical pattern, over a corresponding set of sterilized inoculum cups (Oxoid aluminium test-tube caps).

FIG. 1. Automatic multi-point inoculator without "Perspex" cover.

When a Petri dish is inserted in the right-hand side of the machine and is pushed fully home, a micro-switch is thereby closed and the motor drive is started.

The motor operates a camshaft under the casing of the apparatus, and the cam action then causes the inoculator arm to descend until the inoculator pins are immersed in the cups. Subsequently, the arm rises, pauses, swings over to a position above the Petri dish and descends again. Finally, the arm returns to its original position and the Petri dish is slowly pushed out of the machine so that the operator can immediately cover it with its lid. During the complete cycle the motor circuit is maintained by a second micro-switch, held in the closed position by the main cam. As the cycle finishes the micro-switch reaches a projection on the cam, and all circuits open, so that the machine stops.

Pressing in a second Petri dish then initiates the cycle again, and dishes

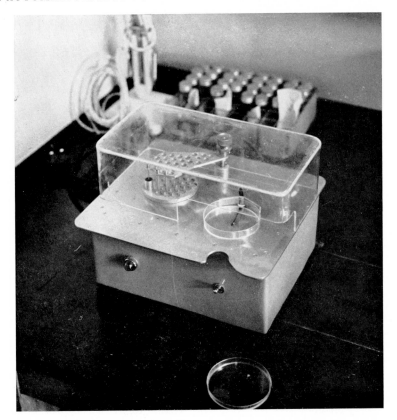

FIG. 2. Automatic multi-point inoculator with "Perspex" cover in position.

may be inserted at 6–7 sec intervals. After use the head, with the inoculating pins in position, is autoclaved.

Tests with the device have shown it to give excellent protection against airborne contamination, and cross-contamination between the contents of cups has rarely presented a problem. The reproducibility of the drop-size delivered by needles of 2 mm diam. was investigated by filling the cups with a dye solution and "inoculating" an agar surface. Discs of agar containing the deposited dye were then removed, dissolved in boiling water, and the dye concentrations estimated spectrophotometrically. The volume delivered was c. 0·0006 ml, with a standard deviation of 13%. The hand-operated apparatus of Beech et al. (1955) has a reported variation of ± 25%.

Uses of the Apparatus

The apparatus described was fitted with twenty-eight inoculating pins. In its present form its main use would appear to be for the rapid sensitivity testing of a large number of bacteria by the agar dilution method, e.g. the screening of a new antibiotic, in any desired range of concentrations, against a large number of strains of one or more species of bacteria. A number of ready-sterilized and assembled heads, complete with inoculating pins and holders containing "Oxoid" caps, would enable a rapid change to a further series of micro-organisms. The advantages of the semi-quantitative agar dilution technique over the tube dilution method and the facilitation of the agar method by use of a mechanical device have been described (Sylvester, 1962). There is no reason why pins narrower or wider than those described above should not be used, if necessary for specific applications; alternatively, suitably mounted platinum loops of appropriate diameter may be substituted for the pins.

The manual application of antibiotic-impregnated filter-paper discs on to inoculated agar surfaces for rapid quantitative sensitivity determinations is a laborious task. Adaptation of our apparatus for this purpose has been achieved by substituting stainless steel tubes for the pins, the steel tubes being attached by flexible tubing to a vacuum manifold. Stacks of prepared discs in suitable holders then replace the required number of cups, and single discs may be transferred in any required pattern to the agar surface by vacuum release. The method described by Stokes (1960), in which an agar plate is inoculated with the specimen to be tested, together with control streaks of *Staphylococcus aureus* (Oxford H) and four discs applied in a set pattern, may thus be simply mechanized. The application of the control staphylococcus may be simplified by substitution of the long edge of a microscope slide for the wire loop, a method described by Barrow and Ellis (1962). For applications requiring sterilization of loops or needles between each transfer, the cycle can be modified so that the loops are passed through a trough of methylated spirit, followed by a gas jet, after each inoculation.

We thank Mrs M. Way and Miss J. Mallion for skilful assistance.

References

BARROW, G. I., & ELLIS, C. (1962). Colicine typing of *Shigella sonnei* by replicate multiple-slide inoculation of indicator organisms. *Mon. Bull. Minist. Hlth Lab. Serv.*, **21**, 141.

BEECH, F. W., CARR, J. G., & CODNER, R. C. (1955). A multipoint inoculator for plating bacteria or yeasts. *J. gen. Microbiol.*, **13**, 408.

GARRETT, S. D. (1946). A multiple-point inoculating needle for agar plates. *Trans. Brit. mycol. Soc.*, **29**, 171.

LIDWELL, O. M. (1959). Apparatus for phage-typing of *Staphylococcus aureus*. *Mon. Bull. Minist. Hlth Lab. Serv.*, **18**, 49.

SMITH, D. A. (1961). A multiple inoculation device for use with fluids. *J. appl. Bact.*, **24,** 131.

STOKES, E. J. (1960). *Clinical Bacteriology*, 2nd ed. London: Edward Arnold Ltd.

SYLVESTER, J. C. (1962). *Antimicrobial Agents and Chemotherapy*. U.S.A. Amer. Soc. Microbiol.

TARR, H. A. (1958). Mechanical aids for the phage-typing of *Staphylococcus aureus. Mon. Bull. Minist. Hlth Lab. Serv.*, **17,** 64.

An Information Sorter for Identifying Bacteria

R. J. OLDS

Department of Pathology, Cambridge, England

Most bacterial diseases of medical or veterinary importance are diagnosed by the isolation and identification of the causative micro-organisms. Standard textbooks (Wilson and Miles, 1964; Cruickshank, 1960; Breed *et al.*, 1957; Kauffmann, 1954) give detailed descriptions of many species, but only a few authors (Stokes, 1960; Willis, 1960; Schaub *et al.*, 1958; Cowan and Steel, 1961) suggest a scheme for identifying an organism from among the many that may be encountered in diagnostic specimens.

Because of the necessity for speed in diagnosis, short-cuts are usually justified. The result is that the common pathogens are recognized promptly, but the less common may need many days' examination. Some organisms, although well described in textbooks, may not be identified, e.g. *Listeria monocytogenes* (Gray, 1962).

Where difficulties arise even the more practical reference books may be unhelpful, and the bacteriologist may have to resort to hit-and-miss methods progressively to eliminate diagnostic possibilities. Bifurcating keys such as those of Breed *et al.* (1957) or Skerman (1957) are often very time-consuming to operate.

The bacteriologist needs a simple means for rapidly sorting the essential information recorded for all recognized pathogens and at the same time comparing this with information obtained about an unknown isolate. This is provided by the information sorter described below.

Description of Sorter

The sorter (Fig. 1) consists of twenty-five superimposed plates, each of which is perforated by 192 holes of 5 mm diam. Each hole represents a bacterium or a group of bacteria.

The top plate carries a plastic window bearing the names of the bacteria to identify the holes. The other twenty-four plates (slides) are suspended between a light source and the top plate.

Each slide represents a test which is used to identify the unknown

FIG. 1. The information sorter. The slide switches are arranged on either side of the window bearing the names of the bacteria. The window is 7 in square.

bacterium, and is controlled by a switch labelled with the name of the test. Each slide can be switched from "neutral" to one of two other positions relative to the top plate. When all slides are in the neutral position, the window is illuminated in all of the 192 positions, so that a small circle of light appears under each bacterial name (Fig. 2).

Apart from the 192 holes corresponding to those of the top plate each slide carries additional holes positioned to record the reaction of each isolate to the test represented by that slide. For example, if the "Gram" slide is moved from the neutral position to the positive position, the names of all Gram-positive organisms will still be illuminated, but the light spots will be removed from the names of all Gram-negative organisms.

Certain holes in the slides are so shaped that special features of the reaction may be recorded. These include: (a) uncommon reactions (i.e.

those given by less than 20% of strains), (b) late, delayed or slow reactions, (c) weak or slight reactions, (d) reactions which occur only in an atmosphere containing added CO_2 or in media containing added growth factors or other supplement. For example, some organisms ferment lactose only after a number of days; some are motile at 28° but not at 37°. Each such special

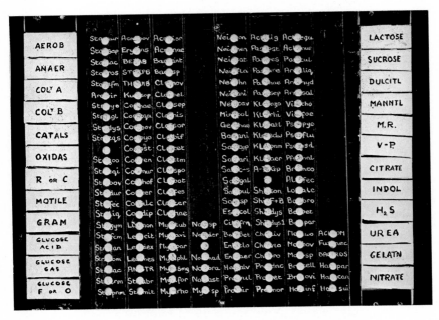

FIG. 2. Front view of the sorter with all slides neutral and the viewing lamp turned on. Each bacterial (or group) name is marked by a circle of light.

feature can be noted readily from the shape of the hole. In each instance the negative reaction is "carried over" so that the organism is not eliminated if, for example, the test is read too early in the case of lactose, or at 37° in the case of motility. A much greater degree of "carry-over" is practicable with the sorter than can be tolerated in conventional tabulated data.

Diagnostic Tests

The twenty-four tests have been selected for their usefulness and speed in identifying organisms likely to be cultivated in medical or veterinary laboratories. These tests can be applied as soon as the result is obtained and in any order. In practice it is found that this rapidly narrows the diagnostic possibilities (Fig. 3). The tests used are: aerobic growth, anaerobic growth, colony characters (divided between two slides), catalase, oxidase, rod or coccus, motility, Gram, glucose acid, glucose gas, glucose fermented or oxidized, lactose acid, sucrose acid, mannitol acid, dulcitol acid, methyl red, Voges-Proskauer, citrate utilization, indole, hydrogen sulphide, urease, gelatin and nitrate. The instrument can be dismantled readily so that additional information can be incorporated by the user.

Of the 192 locations, thirty-five are unused and are reserved for organisms which may be described in the future, or any other organisms or group which the user may wish to add. For instance, it may be found that an organism in a certain geographical area usually gives such atypical reactions that it should be treated as a separate diagnostic problem. Of the 157 locations used, twelve represent groups of organisms which may be broken down by other methods if necessary. The 157 locations store 7536 immediately available bits of information.

The sorter is accompanied by notes which give: (a) the approved procedure for carrying out tests, (b) procedure for breaking down groups,

AEROB	Sta.aur	Acm.bov	Acm.isr		Nei.gon	Act.lig	Act.equ		LACTOSE
	Sta.sap	Ery.ins	Acm.nae		Nei.men	Pas.pst	Act.mur		
ANAER	Sta.lac	BETA8	Bac.ant		Nei.cat	Pas.pes	Pas.tul		SUCROSE
	Sta.afm	STREP8	Ba..sp		Nei.fla	Pas.ure	Arm.lig		
COL' A	Sta.afm	THERM8	Clo.nov		Nei.phn	Pas.hae	Arm.hyd		DULCITL
	Arc.vir	Kur.zop	Clo.wel		Nei.ani	Pas.sep	Arm.sal		
COL' B	Str.pyo	Cor.hae	Clo.sep		Nei.cav	Kle.ozo	Vib.cho		MANNTL
	Str.agl	Cor.equ	Clo.his		Mim.pol	Kle.rhi	Vib.foe		
CATALS	Str.dys	Cor.bov	Clo.sor		Gem.hae	Kle.att	Pse.pyo		M.R.
	Str.eqs	Cor.pyo	Clo.bif		Bac.ani	Kle.edw	Pse.flu		
OXIDAS		Cor.pst	Clo.tet		Sal.typ	Kle.pnm	Pse.psd		V-P
	Str.zoo	Cor.ren	Clo.ttm		Sal.ari	Kle.aer	Pfe.mal		
R or C	Str.eqi	Cor.mur	Clo.spo		Sal.c-s	A-D.Gp	Bru.neo		CITRATE
	Str.bov	Cor.hof	Clo.bot		Sal.gal		Alc.fec		
MOTILE	Str.dur	Cor.xer	Clo.fes		Sal.pul	Shi.son	Lop.alc		INDOL
	Str.fec	Cor.ulc	Clo.ter		Sal-sp	Shi.F+8	Bor.bro		
GRAM	Str.liq	Cor.dip	Clo.hne		Esc.col	Shi.dys	Bor.pet		H₂S
	Str.sym	Lis.mon	Myc.tub	Noc-sp	Cit.frn	Shi.dys1	Bor.par		
GLUCOSE ACID	Str.fcm	Leu.cit	Myc.avi	Noc.der	Bal-Bet	Chr.liv	Mor.lwo	ACHROM	UREA
	Str.san	Leu.dex	Myc.par	Noc.mad	Ent.clo	Chr.vio	Mor.bov	FUS.nec	
GLUCOSE GAS	Str.hom	Leu.mes	Myc.phl	Noc.mad	Ent.aer	Chr.pro	Mor-sp	BACTRDS	GELATN
	Str.lac	AN-STR	Myc.smg	Noc.bra	Haf.alv	Proydnc	Brucell	Hae.par	
GLUCOSE F or O	Str.erm	Str.ubr	Myc.for	Noc.ast	Pro.vul	Pro.ret	Bru.ovi	Hae.can	NITRATE
	Str.pnm	Str.mit	Myc.rho	Myc-sp	Pro.mir	Pro.mor	Hae.inf	Hae.sui	

F ɪ ɢ. 3. A simple problem solved by the sorter. Only three tests are required to identify this unknown. Oxidase +ve, Motility +ve, Gram +ve ——→ *Bacillus sp.*; not *B. anthracis*.

Note that these three switches have been moved to the positive position. This eliminates all other organisms including *B. anthracis*, which occupies the location immediately above *Bacillus sp.*

(c) details of the special features represented by patterned holes, and (d) certain additional information which may assist identification of an unknown.

Although much time has been taken to make the information as complete as possible, most of it agrees with that given by standard reference books. Where information is not available or has been based on too few strains, both negative and positive holes have been punched to ensure that the test concerned is not used as an eliminating character for that organism.

The organisms listed are those likely to be encountered in medical or veterinary laboratories. The method could, of course, be adapted to bacterial (and other) identifications in other fields such as industry or agriculture, but other information and sorting tests would then be used.

Interpretation of Results

In practice one of three results may be obtained:

(1) Usually only one possible identification results. The bacteriologist then has to decide whether this is an unequivocal identification on the basis of these tests, or whether additional confirmatory tests should be used.

(2) Sometimes a number of possible identifications result. If the list included one possible pathogen, the bacteriologist would probably apply selected tests for the pathogen only. If a more detailed examination was required, each of the remaining possibilities might be tested as directed in the notes.

(3) Occasionally no identification results, because all locations are eliminated. One can readily test whether the unknown is indeed one of the organisms represented, but atypical in one character: each slide in turn is switched to the opposite position and any identifications resulting considered. Each switch must be moved back to the original position before proceeding to the next. This procedure takes only a minute or two, and may be useful for detecting atypical strains. (The majority of atypical strains are already allowed for in the punching: strains detected by this test would be very uncommon.) A more complex procedure could be used for detecting a strain atypical in two characters, but this is not advocated, because the probability of such an occurrence is so small.

It is obvious that the decision must remain with the bacteriologist: he should not expect the sorter to make the identification for him. It will assist him by memorizing tedious detail, and by presenting him with a list of organisms to be eliminated before he identifies an unknown. It is flexible in use and he can supplement its information with his own observations at any stage.

The sorter has also proved useful (a) in re-planning standard diagnostic schemes, (b) in devising media and minimal tests for the presumptive identification of an organism in a research project, and (c) as a teaching aid. The process of examining and identifying an organism often enables the bacteriologist to recognize it with less trouble when he meets it again. In this way the teaching and diagnostic functions of the device merge into one another.

It is expected that an improved model will soon be commercially available.

I am indebted to a number of colleagues for helpful discussion; in particular to the late Dr K. J. Steel. The photographs are the work of Mr R. A. Law of Pye Ltd, Cambridge.

References

BREED, R. S., MURRAY, E. G. D., & SMITH, N. R. (1957). *Bergey's Manual of Determinative Bacteriology*. London: Baillière, Tindall & Cox Ltd.

COWAN, S. T., & STEEL, K. J. (1961). Diagnostic tables for the common medical bacteria. *J. Hyg., Camb.*, **59**, 357.

CRUICKSHANK, R. (1960). *Mackie and McCartney's Handbook of bacteriology*. Edinburgh: Livingstone.

GRAY, M. L. (1962). *Listeria monocytogenes* and listeric infection in the diagnostic laboratory. *Ann. N.Y. Acad. Sci.*, **98**, 686.

KAUFFMANN, F. (1954). *Enterobacteriaceae*. Copenhagen: Einar Munksgaard.

SCHAUB, I. G., FOLEY, M. K., SCOTT, E. G., & BAILEY, W. R. (1958). *Diagnostic Bacteriology*. London: Henry Kimpton.

SKERMAN, V. B. D. (1957). A key for the determination of the generic position of organisms: in Breed *et al.* (1957).

STOKES, E. J. (1960). *Clinical Bacteriology*. London: Arnold.

WILLIS, A. T. (1960). *Anaerobic Bacteriology in Clinical Medicine*. London: Butterworth.

WILSON, G. S., & MILES, A. A. (1964). *Topley and Wilson's Principles of Bacteriology and Immunity*. 5th ed. London: Arnold.

Author Index

Numbers in italics are pages on which references are listed at the end of the paper.

Subject Index